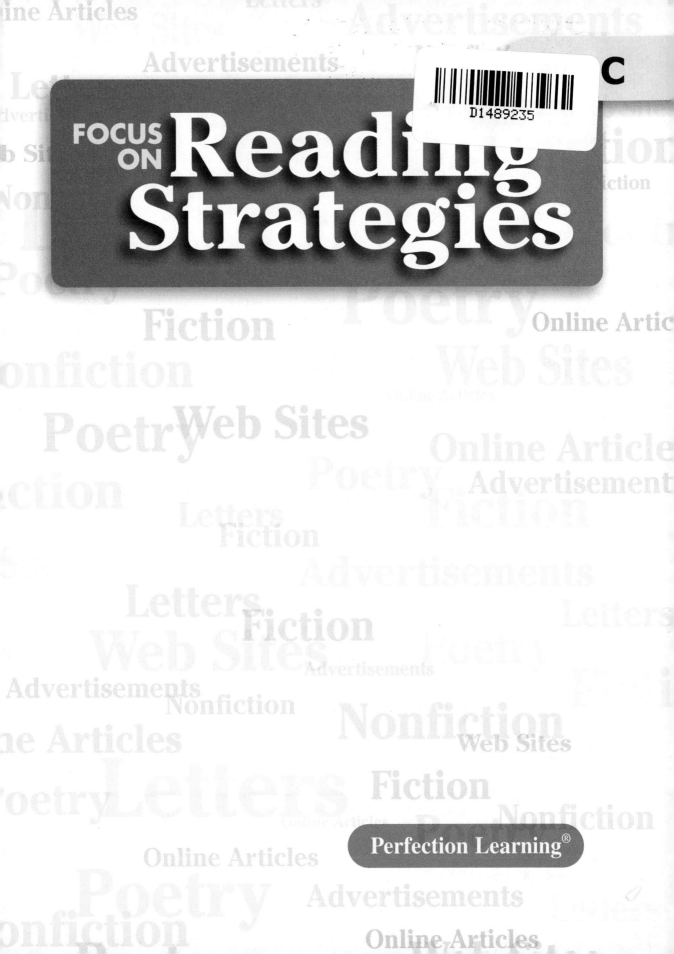

FOCUS ON Reading Strategies

Perfection Learning®

Editorial Director: Susan C. Thies
Editor: Paula J. Reece
Writer: Joan Peterson
Design Director: Randy Messer
Cover Design: Michael A. Aspengren
Book Design: Deborah Lea Bell
Contributing Designers: Emily Greazel, Brianne Osborn,
Sue Bjork-Rush, Wade Thompson, Deb Yoder
Photo Research: Lisa Lorimor

Reviewers:

Kathryn Black
Language Program Specialist
Mesa Public Schools
Mesa, Arizona

Cindy Brunswick
Literacy Coordinator
Center for School Improvement
University of Chicago
Chicago, Illinois

L. Michelle Johnson, M.Ed.
Education Department
Washington College
Chestertown, Maryland

Jan Keese
K–12 Reading Facilitator
Ankeny Community Schools
Ankeny, Iowa

Photo Credits: p. 57 ©Peter Turnkey/CORBIS

Some images www.clipart.com; www.photos.com; Corel Professional Photos;
Dynamic Graphics Liquid Library

For information, contact
Perfection Learning® Corporation
1000 North Second Avenue, P.O. Box 500
Logan, Iowa 51546-0500.
Phone: 1-800-831-4190
Fax: 1-800-543-2745
perfectionlearning.com

ISBN 0-7891-6075-7

3 4 5 6 BA 08 07 06 05

Table of Contents

Section 1

Unit 1: Practice Active Questioning

Lesson 1: Card Games
Expository Nonfiction • Beth Dvergsten Stevens 5

Lesson 2: How Far Away? *from* Tigers at Twilight
Novel Excerpt • Mary Pope Osborne 14

Unit 2: Make Inferences/Draw Conclusions

Lesson 3: *from* Sarah, Plain and Tall
Novel Excerpt • Patricia MacLachlan 24

Lesson 4: Lion Ghosts of Africa
Online Magazine Article • Margaret G. Zackowitz ... 39

Unit 3: Distinguish Fact and Opinion

Lesson 5: Alexa's Letter
Letter to the Editor • Alexa DeVore 48

Lesson 6: Gypsy Life *from* Gypsy in the Cellar
Novel Excerpt • Bonnie Highsmith Taylor 57

Review 1
A Plan for Fame *from* Bigfoot in
New York City?
Novel Excerpt • Dorothy Francis 69

Listening Comprehension 1
School Days
Short Story • Edward Siegel 81

continued

Section 2

Unit 4: Analyze Plot Structure

Lesson 7: Danger at the Pond *from* The Spy Catchers
Novel Excerpt • Dorothy Francis 82

Lesson 8: The Ugly Duckling
Fairy Tale • Hans Christian Andersen
(retold by L. L. Owens) 93

Unit 5: Understand Characterization

Lesson 9: Rebecca: Calvin Coolidge's Raccoon
Narrative Nonfiction • Kathleen Muldoon 107

Lesson 10: Teacher's Pet *from* Marvin Redpost: Alone in
His Teacher's House
Novel Excerpt • Louis Sachar 117

Unit 6: Examine Theme

Lesson 11: The Country Mouse and the Town Mouse
Fable • Aesop (retold by Karen Berg Douglas) 130

Lesson 12: The Duck and the Moon
Poem • Leo Tolstoy 140

Review 2
Johnny Appleseed
American Folktale • retold by Peg Hall 146

Listening Comprehension 2
The Three of Them
Short Story • Edward Siegel 159

Lesson 1

Card Games

• *Expository Nonfiction*

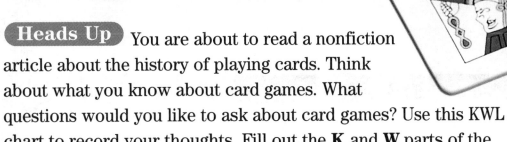

Heads Up You are about to read a nonfiction article about the history of playing cards. Think about what you know about card games. What questions would you like to ask about card games? Use this KWL chart to record your thoughts. Fill out the **K** and **W** parts of the chart now. You will fill out the **L** column after you read the article.

K
(What do I Know?)

_____

_____

_____

_____

_____

continued

W
(What do I Want to find out?)

_____

_____

_____

_____

_____

L
(What did I Learn?)

_____

_____

_____

_____

_____

Good readers think while they read. One way of thinking is by asking yourself questions. As you read "Card Games," you will notice many Think-Along Questions. Stop and answer these questions before you continue reading. Add any questions you have of your own. Also, as you read, circle or highlight any words you don't know.

Card Games

by Beth Dvergsten Stevens

1   You can play many different games with just one deck of cards. But the earliest cards didn't look like the ones we use today.

2   Early cards were flat sticks with special markings. These stick cards were popular in China.

3   As time passed, stick cards changed. The markings were printed on paper strips instead. The oldest paper card ever found was near China. It was about 1,000 years old.

4   Arab soldiers brought cards from China to Spain. By the late 1300s, many people in Europe were playing card games.

5   When **Europeans** came to America, so did decks of cards. How? Probably inside people's pockets!

6   Artists painted the earliest playing cards by hand. They used gold and silver paints.

7   Each deck cost a lot of money. Many people couldn't afford them.

> Why did a deck of cards cost so much?

But kings and queens could buy cards. So the artists made ones that looked like the people who bought them. The faces of kings and queens were painted on the cards! These were called *face cards*.

continued

My Thoughts

8   Today's cards are printed on stiff paper. They don't cost much money.

Why do today's cards cost so little?

The backs have different **designs**. But the faces of all cards are similar. And the face cards still show kings and queens. This style of card is at least 500 years old.

9   Look at a deck of cards. You will see four different suits, or shapes. Spades and clubs are black. Hearts and diamonds are red. Playing cards today look like the cards used in France many years ago.

Where do you think the idea of using spades, clubs, hearts, and diamonds came from?

10   Different countries used other shapes. Germany used acorns, bells, hearts, and leaves. Spain and Italy used batons, coins, cups, and swords.

11   A normal deck has 52 playing cards. There are two extra cards called *jokers*. Sometimes jokers are used as wild cards. That means that jokers are special so they can be used for different purposes.

What do you think was the original purpose of the jokers?

12   Certain games use jokers as the highest card. Or jokers can be the cards worth the most points. Sometimes jokers are used in place of lost cards.

13   Today, a deck of cards can be found in almost every home.

What card games do you play?

Make Sense of Words When you come across an unknown word, you can try to understand the meaning by:

- rereading the sentence and using the *context clues*. This means paying attention to the other words in the sentence and the paragraph.

- breaking the word into parts. A *base word* is the main part of a word. A *prefix* is added to the beginning of a base word to change its meaning. A *suffix* is added to the end of a base word to change its meaning.

- using the dictionary or asking an adult.

Use these three techniques to determine the meaning of two words found in "Card Games."

1. Fill out the chart and answer the following questions.

 a. Find the word **Europeans** in paragraph 5. Reread the sentence. Then fill out the chart below.

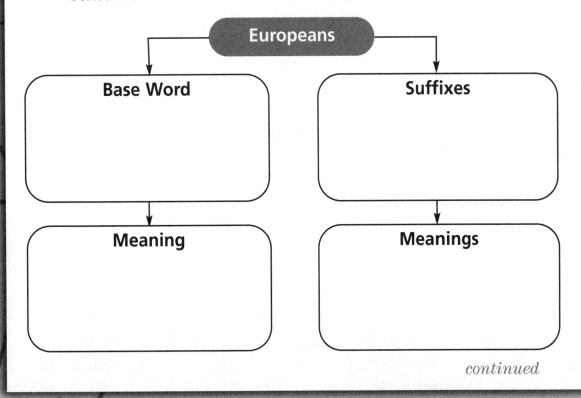

continued

    b. Write the definition based on the base word plus suffixes.

    _____

    c. Give some examples of **Europeans**.

    _____

    d. Could a person from Spain be a **European**? _____

       Explain your answer. _____

       _____

2. Reread paragraph 8 and the sentence "The backs have different **designs**." Then fill in the organizer below.

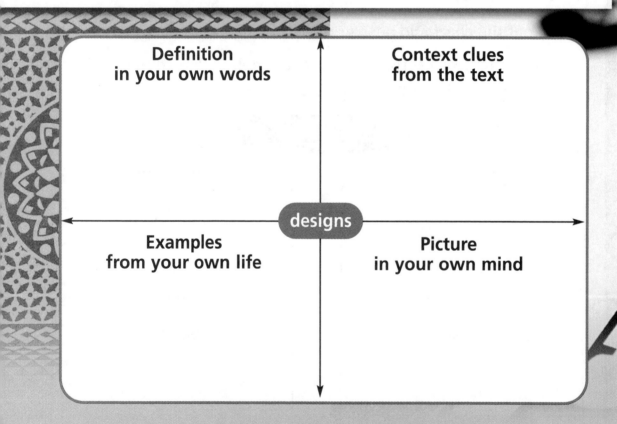

Definition in your own words	Context clues from the text
Examples from your own life	Picture in your own mind

designs

Now look back at any words that you circled in the story. Could you use any of these techniques to figure out what those words mean?

Read with Understanding Were the questions you wrote on your KWL chart in the Heads Up section answered? Add to the **L** part of the chart now.

Read the following questions. Which question could be answered after reading "Card Games"?

① How do you play bridge?

② Why are there face cards?

③ How much does a deck of cards cost?

④ How did Europeans come to America?

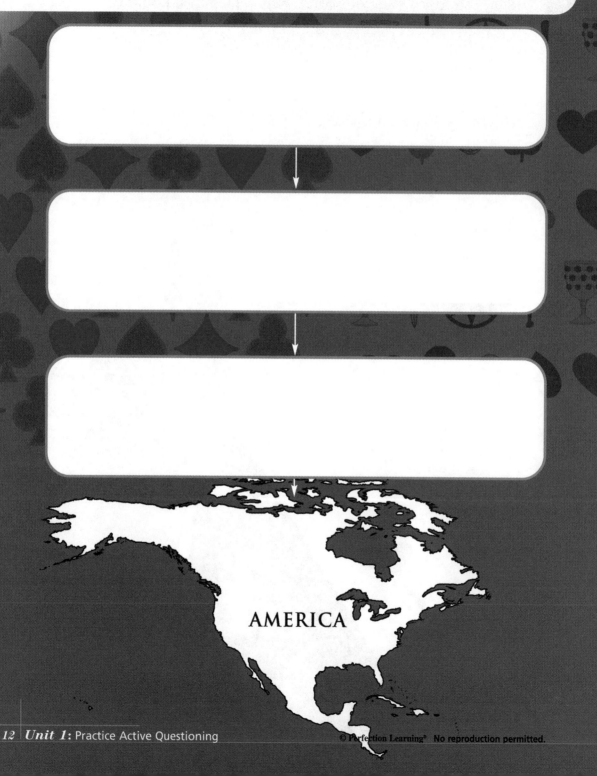

AMERICA

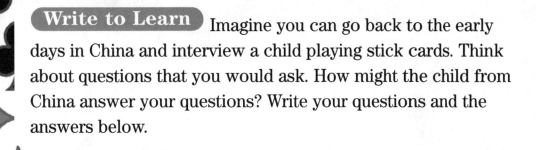

Write to Learn Imagine you can go back to the early days in China and interview a child playing stick cards. Think about questions that you would ask. How might the child from China answer your questions? Write your questions and the answers below.

How Far Away?

from Tigers at Twilight

• *Novel Excerpt*

Heads Up You are about to read a chapter from the novel *Tigers at Twilight*. This is a book in the Magic Tree House series. One day, Jack and his little sister Annie found a mysterious tree house in the woods. When they climbed inside, they saw that it was filled with books. They learned that the tree house was magic and could take them to the places in the books. Their journey began with an adventure in search of a magician. Now they are on a quest to free a dog from a spell.

From this introduction to the book and the title of the chapter, what questions do you have? Write your questions on the next page.

Questions I Have

_____

_____

_____

_____

_____

_____

_____

_____

_____

_____

_____

_____

_____

_____

You will probably find the answers to some of your questions as you read. You may think of other questions as you read too. Good readers ask questions while reading. Answer the Think-Along Questions that you will find in the text. Also, as you read, circle or highlight any words you don't know.

How Far Away?

from Tigers at Twilight

by Mary Pope Osborne

1   Jack and Annie walked past the Frog Creek woods on their way home from the library.

2   "I miss Teddy," said Annie.

Who do you think Teddy is?

3   "Me, too," said Jack.

4   "He's a really smart dog," said Annie.

5   "Yeah," said Jack, "and brave."

6   "And wise," said Annie.

7   "And funny," said Jack.

8   "And here!" said Annie.

9   "What?" said Jack.

10   "*Here!*" Annie pointed at the Frog Creek woods.

11   A small dog with tan-colored fur was peeking out from the bushes.

12   *Arf! Arf!* he barked.

13   "Oh, wow! Teddy!" said Jack.

14   The little dog ran off into the woods.

15   "Let's go!" said Annie.

16   She and Jack raced after Teddy. The Frog Creek woods **glowed** with late afternoon sunlight.

17   The dog ran between the trees and finally stopped at a rope ladder. It hung from the tallest oak tree and led up to the magic tree house.

How do you think the dog knows about the tree house?

18   Teddy waited for Jack and Annie to catch up. He panted and wagged his tail.

19   "Hi, you!" cried Annie. She picked up the little dog and hugged him. "We missed you!"

20   "Yeah, silly!" said Jack. He kissed Teddy. Teddy licked his face.

21   "Is it time to get our *third* gift?" asked Annie.

22   Teddy sneezed, as if to say, *Of course!*

23   Annie grabbed the rope ladder and started up. Jack put Teddy inside his backpack and followed.

24   They climbed into the tree house. There was the note from Morgan le Fay. It was on the floor, just where it had been two days ago.

> **Who do you think Morgan le Fay is?**

25   Jack let Teddy out of his pack.

26   Annie picked up the note and read:

This little dog is under a spell and needs your help. To free him, you must be given four special things:

A gift from a ship lost at sea,
A gift from the prairie blue,
A gift from a forest far away,
A gift from a kangaroo.
Be wise. Be brave. Be careful.
Morgan

27   Jack touched the first two gifts, which they had already gotten: a pocket watch from the *Titanic* and an eagle's feather from the Lakota Indians of the Great Plains.

continued

How Far Away? continued

My Thoughts

28   "Now we have to get the gift from a forest far away," said Annie.

> Where could they find a forest?

29   "I wonder *how* far away?" said Jack.

30   "I know how to find out," said Annie. "Where's our book?"

31   She and Jack looked around the tree house for one of the research books that Morgan always left them.

32   *Arf! Arf!* Teddy pawed a book in the corner.

33   Jack picked it up and read the title: *Wildlife of India.*

34   "Oh, man. India," he said. "That's *very* far away."

35   "Let's get going," said Annie, "so we can free Teddy."

36   Jack pointed at the cover of the book.

37   "I wish we could go there," he said.

38   The wind started to blow.

39   The tree house started to spin.

> What do you think is happening?

40   It spun faster and faster.

41   Then everything was still.

42   Absolutely still.

43   But only for a moment . . .

> Where do you think Jack and Annie will find themselves?

Make Sense of Words When you come across an unknown word, you can try to understand the meaning by:

- rereading the sentence and using the *context clues*. This means paying attention to the other words in the sentence and the paragraph.

- breaking the word into parts. A *base word* is the main part of a word. A *prefix* is added to the beginning of a base word to change its meaning. A *suffix* is added to the end of a base word to change its meaning.

- using the dictionary or asking an adult.

1. Reread the sentence in paragraph 16, "The Frog Creek woods **glowed** with late afternoon sunlight."

   a. Write down a prediction about what **glowed** means.

   _____

   _____

   b. Use the dictionary. Write the definition of **glow**. (Remember, the dictionary only has present tense words.)

   _____

   _____

   c. Write your own sentence using the word **glowed**.

   _____

   _____

   continued

Make Sense of Words *continued*

d. Illustrate this sentence: "The Frog Creek woods **glowed** with late afternoon sunlight."

My picture of the Frog Creek woods

Now look back at any words that you circled in the story. Could you use any of these techniques to figure out what those words mean?

Read with Understanding You asked yourself many questions while reading "How Far Away?" Which question below could be answered after reading this chapter?

① How big are the Frog Creek woods?

② How old are Annie and Jack?

③ Who built the tree house?

④ How many special things do Annie and Jack need to find?

Understand by Seeing It Look back at the note the kids found in the tree house. You may have some questions about the four special gifts the note mentions. Fill in the organizer below with the phrase about each gift. This may help to make the note clearer to you. Then fill in the first two gifts that Annie and Jack have already found. Predict, by using the clues in the note, a gift from the forest and a gift from a kangaroo. Write your predictions in the boxes under Gift 3 and Gift 4.

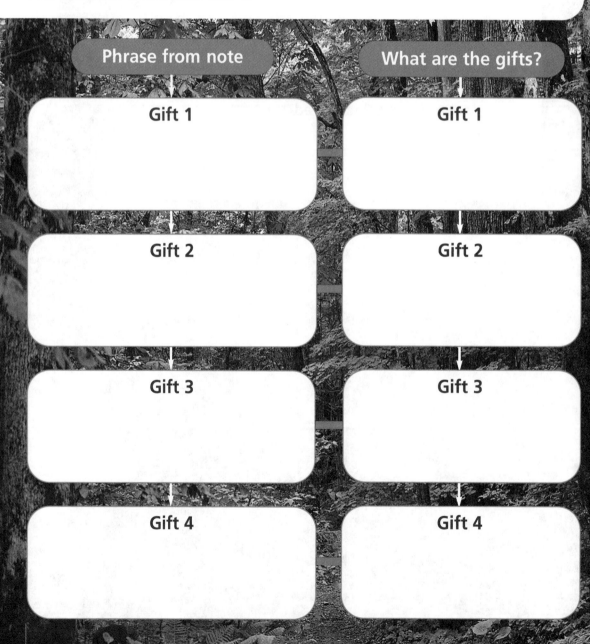

Phrase from note

What are the gifts?

| Gift 1 | Gift 1 |

| Gift 2 | Gift 2 |

| Gift 3 | Gift 3 |

| Gift 4 | Gift 4 |

Write to Learn You probably have many questions about what will happen to Jack and Annie. Write a paragraph describing what you think will happen during their adventure.

Lesson 3

from
Sarah, Plain and Tall

• *Novel Excerpt*

Heads Up You are about to read Chapter 1 from *Sarah, Plain and Tall*. As you read, look for details about the characters or events provided by the author. Sometimes authors don't tell you all you want to know about the characters and events. When this happens, you can combine the facts from the author with information that you already know. This is called *drawing conclusions* or *making inferences*.

Quickly skim through Chapter 1 of *Sarah, Plain and Tall*, without reading it, and choose ten words that you predict will be key words. Record those words on the next page. Then, based on those words, predict what the story is going to be about. Write your prediction on the next page.

My Key Words

_____   _____

_____   _____

_____   _____

_____   _____

_____

My Prediction

_____

_____

_____

_____

_____

_____

Practice active reading by asking yourself
questions about the characters, setting,
and events as you read. Answering
the Think-Along Questions should
help you get started. Also, as
you read, circle or highlight
any words you don't know.

from
Sarah, Plain and Tall

by Patricia MacLachlan

1   "Did Mama sing every day?" asked Caleb. "Every-single-day?" He sat close to the fire, his chin in his hand. It was dusk, and the dogs lay beside him on the warm hearthstones.

2   "Every-single-day," I told him for the second time this week. For the twentieth time this month. The hundredth time this year? And the past few years?

Who do you think the person who uses "I" is?

3   "And did Papa sing, too?"

4   "Yes. Papa sang, too. Don't get so close, Caleb. You'll heat up."

5   He pushed his chair back. It made a hollow scraping sound on the hearthstones, and the dogs stirred. Lottie, small and black, wagged her tail and lifted her head. Nick slept on.

6   I turned the bread dough over and over on the marble slab on the kitchen table.

7   "Well, Papa doesn't sing anymore," said Caleb very softly. A log broke apart and crackled in the fireplace. He looked up at me. "What did I look like when I was born?"

8   "You didn't have any clothes on," I told him.

9   "I know that," he said.

10   "You looked like this." I held the bread dough up in a round pale ball.

11   "I had hair," said Caleb seriously.

12   "Not enough to talk about," I said.

13   "And she named me Caleb," he went on, filling in the old familiar story.

Who is "she"?

14   "*I* would have named you Troublesome," I said, making Caleb smile.

Draw a conclusion as to why the narrator would call Caleb "Troublesome."

15   "And Mama handed me to you in the yellow blanket and said . . ." He waited for me to finish the story. "And said . . . ?"

16   I sighed. "And Mama said, 'Isn't he beautiful, Anna?' "

17   "And I was," Caleb finished.

18   Caleb thought the story was over, and I didn't tell him what I had really thought. He was homely and plain, and he had a terrible holler and a horrid smell. But these were not the worst of him. Mama died the next morning. That was the worst thing about Caleb.

19   "Isn't he beautiful, Anna?" Her last words to me. I had gone to bed thinking how **wretched** he looked. And I forgot to say good night.

continued

from Sarah, Plain and Tall continued

My Thoughts

20   I wiped my hands on my apron and went to the window. Outside, the prairie reached out and touched the places where the sky came down. Though winter was nearly over, there were patches of snow and ice everywhere. I looked at the long dirt road that crawled across the plains, remembering the morning that Mama had died, cruel and sunny. They had come for her in a wagon and taken her away to be buried. And then the cousins and aunts and uncles had come and tried to fill up the house. But they couldn't.

21   Slowly, one by one, they left. And then the days seemed long and dark like winter days, even though it wasn't winter. And Papa didn't sing.

22   *Isn't he beautiful, Anna?*

23   *No, Mama.*

24   It was hard to think of Caleb as beautiful. It took three whole days for me to love him, sitting in the chair by the fire, Papa washing up the supper dishes, Caleb's tiny hand brushing my cheek. And a smile. It was the smile, I know.

25   "Can you remember her songs?" asked Caleb. "Mama's songs?"

26   I turned from the window. "No. Only that she sang about flowers and birds. Sometimes about the moon at nighttime."

27   Caleb reached down and touched Lottie's head.

28   "Maybe," he said, his voice low, "if you remember the songs, then I might remember her, too."

29   My eyes widened and tears came. Then the door opened and wind blew in with Papa, and I went to stir the stew. Papa put his arms around me and put his nose in my hair.

> Where do you suppose Anna learned to make stew and bread?

30   "Nice soapy smell, that stew," he said.

31   I laughed. "That's my hair."

32   Caleb came over and threw his arms around Papa's neck and hung down as Papa swung him back and forth, and the dogs sat up.

33   "Cold in town," said Papa. "And Jack was **feisty**." Jack was Papa's horse that he'd raised from a colt. "Rascal," murmured Papa, smiling, because no matter what Jack did Papa loved him.

34   I spooned up the stew and lighted the oil lamp and we ate with the dogs crowding under the table, hoping for spills or handouts.

35   Papa might not have told us about Sarah that night if Caleb hadn't asked him the question. After the dishes were cleared and washed and Papa was filling the tin pail with ashes, Caleb spoke up. It wasn't a question, really.

> Draw a conclusion about where Papa got the ashes to put in the tin pail.

continued

My Thoughts

36   "You don't sing anymore," he said. He said it harshly. Not because he meant to, but because he had been thinking of it for so long. "Why?" he asked more gently.

37   Slowly Papa straightened up. There was a long silence, and the dogs looked up, wondering at it.

38   "I've forgotten the old songs," said Papa quietly. He sat down. "But maybe there's a way to remember them." He looked up at us.

Why do you think Papa forgot the songs?

39   "How?" asked Caleb eagerly.

40   Papa leaned back in the chair. "I've placed an advertisement in the newspapers. For help."

41   "You mean a housekeeper?" I asked, surprised.

42   Caleb and I looked at each other and burst out laughing, remembering Hilly, our old housekeeper. She was round and slow and shuffling. She snored in a high whistle at night, like a teakettle, and let the fire go out.

Why would it be bad to let the fire go out?

43   "No," said Papa slowly. "Not a housekeeper." He paused. "A wife."

44   Caleb stared at Papa. "A wife? You mean a mother?"

45   Nick slid his face onto Papa's lap and Papa stroked his ears.

46   "That, too," said Papa. "Like Maggie."

47   Matthew, our neighbor to the south, had written to ask for a wife and mother for his children. And Maggie had come from Tennessee. Her hair was the color of turnips and she laughed.

What color do you think turnips are?

48   Papa reached into his pocket and unfolded a letter written on white paper. "And I have received an answer." Papa read to us:

49   Dear Mr. Jacob Witting,

I am Sarah Wheaton from Maine as you will see from my letter. I am answering your advertisement. I have never been married, though I have been asked. I have lived with an older brother, William, who is about to be married. His wife-to-be is young and energetic.

I have always loved to live by the sea, but at this time I feel a move is necessary. And the truth is, the sea is as far east as I can go. My choice, as you can see, is limited. This should not be taken as an insult. I am strong and I work hard, and I am willing to travel. But I am not mild mannered. If you should still care to write, I would be interested in your children and about where you live. And you.

Very truly yours,

Sarah Elisabeth Wheaton

P.S. Do you have opinions on cats? I have one.

continued

My Thoughts

> Why do you think Sarah writes that she has been asked to marry in the past?

50   No one spoke when Papa finished the letter. He kept on looking at it in his hands, reading it over to himself. Finally I turned my head a bit to sneak a look at Caleb. He was smiling. I smiled, too.

51   "One thing," I said in the quiet of the room.

52   "What's that?" asked Papa, looking up.

53   I put my arm around Caleb.

54   "Ask her if she sings," I said.

> Why do you suppose Anna wants to know if Sarah sings?

Make Sense of Words When you come across an unknown word, you can try to understand the meaning by:

- rereading the sentence and using the *context clues*. This means paying attention to the other words in the sentence and the paragraph.

- breaking the word into parts. A *base word* is the main part of a word. A *prefix* is added to the beginning of a base word to change its meaning. A *suffix* is added to the end of a base word to change its meaning.

- using the dictionary or asking an adult.

1. In paragraph 19, locate the word **wretched**. **Wretched** is an adjective used by Anna to describe Caleb after he was born.

   a. Make a list of other words in the story Anna uses to describe Caleb. These will be context clues for the meaning of **wretched**.

   b. What do you think **wretched** means?

   c. Look up **wretched** in the dictionary, and write the definition.

continued

    d. *Synonyms* are words that have the same, or nearly the same, meaning. Think of synonyms of **wretched** that Anna could also use to describe Caleb. Write them below.

_____

_____

2. In paragraph 33, find the word **feisty**. **Feisty** is also an adjective. It is used by Papa to describe his horse, Jack.

    a. Look up **feisty** in the dictionary. Write the definition below.

_____

_____

    b. Draw a picture of Jack being **feisty**.

My picture of Jack

Now look back at any words that you circled in the story. Could you use any of these techniques to figure out what those words mean?

Read with Understanding You have read Chapter 1 of *Sarah, Plain and Tall* and paid attention to the details. You have combined those details with information that you already know. Read the following four sentences. Draw a *conclusion* about what will be in Chapter 2 of *Sarah, Plain and Tall*.

① Anna's father will hire someone to help him with the farmwork.

② Anna's family will write back to Sarah.

③ Caleb will go to school to learn some songs.

④ Anna and Caleb will get a new dog.

Understand by Seeing It You have been focusing on *inferences* in this lesson. Remember that an inference is an educated guess. You take details from a story and add them to what you already know to make an inference. Look below at the inference diagram for what you know about Sarah so far from her letter.

What the author says about Sarah

- Sarah is from Maine.
- Sarah is willing to travel.
- Sarah can work hard.
- Sarah has a cat.

What I already know

- Maine is on the ocean.
- People who are willing to travel are adventurous.
- People who are hard workers are responsible.
- Pet owners are caring people.

What I can infer about Sarah

- Sarah has probably seen seashells.
- Sarah is probably adventurous.
- Sarah is probably responsible.
- Sarah is probably caring.

Now make an inference diagram to show what kind of person you think Papa is.

What the author says about Papa

What I already know

What I can infer about Papa

Write to Learn Imagine that you are Caleb. Use the author's descriptions of Caleb and your own knowledge to *infer* some questions that Caleb would have for Sarah. Make a list of questions you think Caleb would ask her. Then organize your list into a letter from Caleb to Sarah.

My Questions

_____

_____

_____

Dear Sarah,

_____

_____

_____

_____

_____

_____

_____

_____

Caleb Witting

Lesson 4

Lion Ghosts of Africa

• *Online Magazine Article*

Heads Up You are about to read an article from the online magazine *National Geographic for Kids*. Based on the title and the magazine the article was featured in, what can you *infer* about the story? Circle one statement below from each pair that you *infer* is true about the story.

- This is a true story.
- This is a made-up story.

- This story's purpose is to scare readers.
- This story's purpose is to educate readers.

- This story will mainly be about ghosts.
- This story will mainly be about lions.

As you are reading, be sure to ask yourself questions about the story. Stopping to answer the Think-Along Questions as you read will help you better understand the article. Also, as you read, circle or highlight any words you don't know.

Lion Ghosts of Africa

by Margaret G. Zackowitz

1   Building a new railroad was hot, hard, dangerous work. In just nine months, some 135 men died. But these men weren't killed on the job.

Infer how the men were killed.

2   The workers were killed and eaten by lions. The railroad project was in Kenya, in East Africa. The year was 1898. The man-eaters were two large maneless male lions.

Why do you think the lions were maneless?

They struck at night in the railroad workers' camps, pulling screaming victims from their tents. The cats seemed to appear out of nowhere. They attacked without warning, then disappeared back into the night. Some people called them ghosts. Legends about the mysterious lions continue today.

Why do you think the lions came out at night?

Hunting the Hunters

3   Even high, thorny wood fences around the workers' camps in the Tsavo River area did not stop the big cats. They jumped over the fences and dragged their prey right through the thorns to escape. No one knew where they would strike next. John Patterson, the railroad

project's supervisor, felt responsible for the safety of the workers, so he went after the lions. For weeks he stalked the pair, but they always managed to **elude** him.

How do you think the lions "eluded" Patterson?

Stories grew about the lions' cleverness. Their nightly killings continued.

Night Stalkers

4   Desperate to stop the attacks, Patterson tried a new approach. He built a platform high up in a tree and used a donkey carcass as bait below. Hiding on the platform, he waited. One of the huge lions showed up that night, but he wasn't interested in the donkey.

Why do you think the lion wasn't interested in the donkey?

The lion went after Patterson, who fired several shots at the cat. The wounded animal disappeared into the bushes.

5   The next morning, trackers found the lion— dead. That still left one killer lion on the loose.

6   Three weeks later Patterson finally killed the second lion. Six bullets hit that big cat before it died. Those lions were so terrifying that more than a century later stories and legends about the man-eaters continue. Some people wonder whether these lions and their descendants are a separate **species** with a taste for humans.

continued

Lion Ghosts of Africa continued

Research Revelations

7   Tsavo's maneless lions were—and are—real, not ghosts. And they aren't a separate species of man-eating lions, although they do tend to be larger than other lions. Their size helps them bring down Cape buffalo, the main prey of lions in Tsavo East, in Tsavo National Park.

How would being bigger help these lions?

My Thoughts

8   Among the scientists studying the lions today, Craig Packer and Peyton West focus on how and why the eastern Tsavo lions are different from the more familiar maned lions. Their studies reveal that maneless lions probably adapted in several ways to better deal with their environment, which is harsher and hotter than that of western Tsavo and the nearby Serengeti region. The scientists believe that one reason these lions evolved to be maneless was that a collar of hair would simply be too hot.

9   Meanwhile other researchers continued trying to determine the truth about why the two killer lions went after humans. They recently discovered that both lions' skulls showed severe tooth injury. Could painful teeth have made it hard for the cats to kill their normal prey? Another piece to the puzzle may be that an outbreak of disease in the early 1890s killed many of Tsavo's hoofed animals. The two man-eaters may simply have had little choice but to eat humans. No one knows for sure.

Make Sense of Words When you come across an unknown word, you can try to understand the meaning by:

- rereading the sentence and using the *context clues*. This means paying attention to the other words in the sentence and the paragraph.

- breaking the word into parts. A *base word* is the main part of a word. A *prefix* is added to the beginning of a base word to change its meaning. A *suffix* is added to the end of a base word to change its meaning.

- using the dictionary or asking an adult.

1. In paragraph 3, locate the word **elude**. It is found in the sentence "For weeks he stalked the pair, but they always managed to **elude** him."

    a. List some words or phrases that would make sense to substitute for **elude**.

    _____

    _____

    _____

    _____

    _____

    b. Look up **elude** in the dictionary, and write its definition.

    _____

    _____

continued

   c. Write your own sentence using the word **elude**.

   _____

   _____

2. In paragraph 6, find the word **species**.
   The definition of **species** is "a class of beings having the same qualities."

Below is a list of animals. All of them are of the same **species** except for one. Cross out the animal that is not of the same **species** as the rest.

Collie

Siamese

Bulldog

Cocker Spaniel

Pit Bull

German Shepherd

Now look back at any words that you circled in the story. Could you use any of these techniques to figure out what those words mean?

Read with Understanding While reading "Lion Ghosts of Africa," you noticed details in the story and combined them with what you know about lions. Read the sentences below. Choose the sentence that could *not* be concluded about maneless lions.

① Maneless lions all have bad teeth.

② Maneless lions are larger than other lions.

③ Maneless lions are very strong.

④ Maneless lions do not seem to be afraid of humans.

Understand by Seeing It An inference diagram can help you better understand what an author writes. By combining what an author says with what you already know, you can draw some smart *conclusions*. Fill out the diagram below.

What the author says about lions.

_____

_____

_____

_____

_____

_____

What I already know about lions.

_____

_____

_____

_____

_____

What I can infer about lions.

_____

_____

_____

Lesson 5

Alexa's Letter

- *Letter to the Editor*

Heads Up You are about to read a letter written by a third grader. The letter contains some facts and some opinions. *Facts* are statements that can be proved. *Opinions* are someone's thoughts or feelings and can't be proved. Facts will stay the same from person to person. But opinions will change depending on whom you ask or even sometimes when you ask.

For example:

- A fact is:
  Third grade is part of the elementary school.

- Joe's opinion may be:
  Third grade is easy.

- Jill's opinion could be:
  Third grade is hard.

Opinions about third grade will vary from person to person. In this letter, Alexa's opinion is "Third grade is not fun anymore."

In the space below, write some *facts* about your class (such as how many students there are, where your school is, etc.).

Facts About My Class

_____

_____

_____

_____

Talk to some of your classmates and find out their *opinions* on your class. Write their opinions in the space below.

Opinions About My Class

_____

_____

_____

_____

Read Alexa's letter. Identify some facts and some opinions. Be sure to ask yourself questions and answer the Think-Along Questions as you read. Also, as you read, circle or highlight any words you don't know.

Alexa's Letter

My Thoughts

1 Dear Editor of *East Elementary Times,*

2   It's not fair that the school took away our noon recess. That's the best part of the day!

> Is this a fact or Alexa's opinion?

I think they should let us have it back.

3   The principal told our class that the teachers need to use that time to help us practice our reading. Our reading scores have fallen. I love reading, but I love recess more. Our principal is just being mean. She doesn't understand that we need recess.

> What is a fact in paragraph 3?

4   We still have an afternoon recess. But this isn't enough! Recess helps us get out some extra energy. It helps us focus during our lessons. Without recess, many kids will talk more. They won't be able to stay in their seats. More kids will get into trouble.

5   Plus, our teacher just told us that he thinks many of us don't get enough exercise. He said we don't play outside enough.

> Do you think the teacher is basing his statement on fact or opinion? Why?

We sit inside and watch cartoons or play video games instead. He told us it was good for us to run around and play. But now our principal is taking away our chance to do that!

6   The best thing to do at recess is play football. Some of the other girls and I have formed a team.

> **Which of Alexa's previous two statements is a fact? Which one is an opinion?**

Without our noon recess, we won't have much time to play anymore. Our afternoon recess isn't long enough to get in a game.

7   Studying is important. But so is our health!

> **How could studying be unhealthy?**

It's good for us to run around. How will students be able to read when they have been **cooped up** inside all morning? This will make some kids hate reading even more.

8   I believe that this is not a good idea. I bet there are other ways we can practice reading without taking away our recess time. I hate spelling. Maybe we can read instead of taking spelling tests! This plan is just going to cause too many problems.

9   Sincerely,
Alexa DeVore
Room 3D

> **Which do you think better helped Alexa's argument— her facts or her opinions? Why?**

My Thoughts

Make Sense of Words When you come across an unknown word, you can try to understand the meaning by:

- rereading the sentence and using the *context clues*. This means paying attention to the other words in the sentence and the paragraph.

- breaking the word into parts. A *base word* is the main part of a word. A *prefix* is added to the beginning of a base word to change its meaning. A *suffix* is added to the end of a base word to change its meaning.

- using the dictionary or asking an adult.

1. Find the phrase **cooped up** in paragraph 7 of "Alexa's Letter." **Cooped up** is an expression. A **coop** is a cage for chickens or other small animals.

   a. What do you think the expression **cooped up** means?

   _____

   _____

   b. Reread the sentence from "Alexa's Letter" below. What word could you substitute for **cooped up**?

   > "How will students be able to read when they have been
   >
   > _____ inside all morning?"
   > **(cooped up)**

Now look back at any words that you circled in the story. Could you use any of these techniques to figure out what those words mean?

Read with Understanding   In her letter, Alexa states some *facts* and some *opinions*. Below are four statements. Three of them are facts. They can be proved. Select the sentence that is Alexa's *opinion*.

① Noon recess is the best part of the day.

② Reading scores have fallen.

③ Many students watch cartoons and play video games after school.

③ Alexa is in third grade.

Understand by Seeing It One method for helping to understand fact and opinion is to use a Fact and Opinion Array. Look at "Alexa's Letter" again. Find three more facts from the letter to write on the lines around *Fact*. (The first fact is written for you.) Then find four opinions to write on the lines around *Alexa's Opinion*. You may add more lines if you wish.

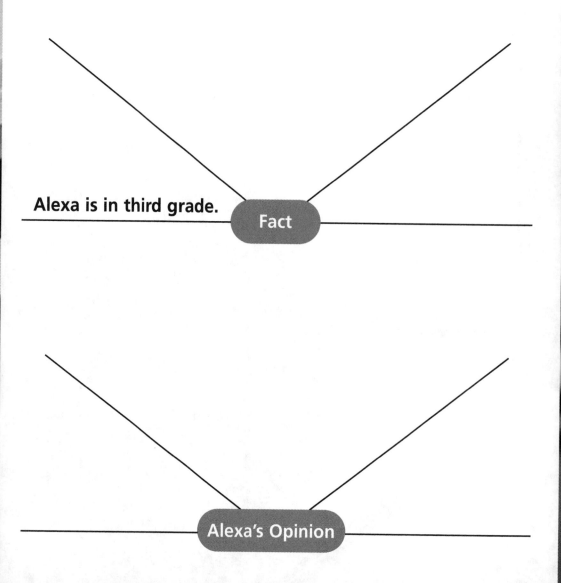

Alexa is in third grade.

Fact

Alexa's Opinion

Imagine that your principal has decided to do away with an activity in your school. It is your job to write a letter, hoping to convince the principal to keep the activity. Write the activity below. List some statements that are *facts* about the importance of it. Then list some *opinion* statements about it.

Activity: _____

Facts

_____

_____

_____

_____

_____

Opinions

_____

_____

_____

_____

_____

continued

Write to Learn *continued*

Now organize your facts and opinions into a short letter to your principal. Remember to use commas after the greeting and the closing as Alexa did.

Lesson 6

Gypsy Life

- *Novel Excerpt*

Heads Up You are about to read "Gypsy Life," which is the first chapter in a novel called *Gypsy in the Cellar*. As you read, look for *facts* that can be proved and *opinions*. An opinion is someone's feeling or belief. Some phrases that help signal an opinion are "I feel," "I think," and "in my opinion." Many times an opinion will also use comparing words such as *best*, *most*, or *prettiest*.

continued

Heads Up *continued*

Below are some statements. Decide if they are fact or opinion. Write an *F* for fact or *O* for opinion in the blank before each statement.

_____ 1. Third grade comes after second grade.

_____ 2. Third grade is the **best** grade.

_____ 1. Each third-grade classroom has at least one teacher.

_____ 2. Third-grade teachers are the **smartest** teachers.

_____ 1. Math is a subject in school.

_____ 2. School is **easy**.

$5 \times 6 = \underline{\qquad}$

Were you able to decide if each sentence is a *fact* or an *opinion*? You probably noticed that each sentence 1 is a fact and can be proved. Each sentence 2 is someone's opinion. The words that help you decide that the statements are opinions are bolded.

As you read this novel excerpt, answer the Think-Along Questions. They will help you focus on fact and opinion. Also, as you read, circle or highlight any words you don't know.

Gypsy Life

from Gypsy in the Cellar

by Bonnie Highsmith Taylor

1   My name is Doreen, and I am a Gypsy. I live with my grandmother and my brother, Frankie. Also my Uncle Alex and the woman he married last summer. And she has three kids that live with us too.

2   I hardly remember my mother. She died when I was only five. I'm not sure where my father is. But I think he's in jail.

3   I asked Grandmother about my father. She said, "It makes no difference. You have a family."

4   When I ask Uncle Alex, he just laughs. "I'll be your father forever and ever," he always says. Uncle Alex was in jail once. But only for a little while.

> **Why do you think Uncle Alex was in jail only a little while?**

5   I don't live any certain place. Gypsies like to travel around. It's nice in the summers. We camp most of the time at the edge of small towns or in the woods by rivers and streams. Lots of families camp together. So there are plenty of kids to play with.

6   When it's warm, we sleep on the ground under the sky. I like to lie awake and look at the moon and stars.

7   Sometimes when everyone else is asleep, I sing to myself. I guess there's not much I like better than singing. Especially at night when there's a little breeze blowing. It sounds so good.

> **What is Doreen's opinion about camping?**

continued

Gypsy Life continued

8   One night I was lying awake singing, and a cat came into our camp. It climbed right in bed with me! I held it tight for a long time. Then it scratched me, so I slapped it. And then it ran off.

9   Cats carry ringworms. Frankie and I had ringworms once. They're awful. Frankie had to have all his hair cut off. He looked like a little, old, bald man.

10   The school nurse made us stay out of school for the rest of the year. That part was nice. I don't like school very much. I've been to a lot of schools. They're all the same. Besides, most of them are in the city.

11   In the winters we usually have to live in the city. We live in empty store buildings most of the time. Sometimes we live in motor courts. But store buildings are better. They don't cost as much. And they are so big that three or four families can live together.

12   One time we lived in a house. For three days, I think. It was a beautiful house. It had beds that were off the floor. And it had a stove that cooked with the turn of a knob. Grandmother was scared of the stove.

13   "It's an evil spirit!" she screamed when Uncle Alex made the flame go high.

14   Uncle Alex and Frankie laughed at her. I tried to laugh. But I was really scared of it too.

15   It was in the middle of the night when the police came. They didn't knock or anything.

They just broke in the door. Then they started pulling us out of bed and swearing at us.

16   I fell and bumped my head on a chair. My head started bleeding.

17   Grandmother flew at one of the policemen. She scratched his face and tore some buttons off his coat. He called her a bad name and pushed her down. Another one put handcuffs on Uncle Alex.

18   "Filthy Gypsies!" they yelled. "Dirty, sneaking thieves! We'll see to it the owners press charges when they get back."

> What is your opinion of Gypsies staying in other people's homes?

19   That was when Uncle Alex went to jail. They were going to put Grandmother in jail. But one of the policemen said, "Then the welfare will be stuck with these two." He looked right at Frankie and me. "Lice and filth and all. They'll have to **fumigate** the house as it is."

20   I hated policemen after that. They were another thing that was bad about the city. The city was full of Gajos. Gajos are people who aren't Gypsies. I hated all of them. Well, I did until last fall.

> What facts have you learned about Gypsies so far?

continued

My Thoughts

21   The rains had started. We had to leave the nice place out in the country and move to a city I had never been to before. Uncle Alex and Grandmother had been there but not for a long time.

22   Grandmother didn't like the fall. It rained so much that it made her **rheumatism** worse. Even the little bag of burdock seeds she wore around her neck didn't help.

23   But Uncle Alex said it was a good place to make a living. His new wife had relatives there, and she liked it.

24   The store building we moved into was small. Smaller than most of the others we had lived in. Grandmother draped her old bedspread and curtains in one corner by the window. That made it very crowded. And hardly any light shone in at all.

25   The corner was for Grandmother's office. This was where she told fortunes. Grandmother was a *dukkerer*.

26   Gypsy women can get a fortune-telling license at the city hall. Then the police don't give them any trouble. Just as long as they don't cheat the Gajos. But Gajos are easy to cheat. They think Gypsies are stupid.

What is a *dukkerer*?

27   Grandmother's fortune-telling name was Madame Sedenia. My mother had been a dukkerer. I guess I will be too, when I'm grown.

It is the best way for a Gypsy woman to make a living. I have already practiced telling fortunes on Frankie and some of the other younger children.

28   One time I foretold that Frankie would go on a long journey and face great danger. And guess what—he did! He hitched a ride on a streetcar and got lost in the other end of town. A policeman and a **truant officer** brought him home late that night.

29   They threatened Grandmother. "See that the child is sent to school and kept off the streets," they ordered. "Or the welfare will take him away."

30   Grandmother wept and threw herself into the arms of the truant officer. "Oh, please, kind one," she begged. "The child will be justly punished and sent to school every day."

31   After the two men left, she held Frankie close and laughed. "Bad boy, you got caught." Then she shook her fist at the closed door and shouted, "Rotten Gajos!"

32   When she opened her fist, I saw something bright and shiny. There were initials on it. It was a cigarette lighter. Grandmother smiled and buried it deep in the pocket of her skirt.

What is Grandmother's opinion of Gajos?

Make Sense of Words When you come across an unknown word, you can try to understand the meaning by:

- rereading the sentence and using the *context clues*. This means paying attention to the other words in the sentence and the paragraph.

- breaking the word into parts. A *base word* is the main part of a word. A *prefix* is added to the beginning of a base word to change its meaning. A *suffix* is added to the end of a base word to change its meaning.

- using the dictionary or asking an adult.

1. Find the word **fumigate** in paragraph 19 of "Gypsy Life."
The police officer looked at the children and said, "Lice and filth and all. They'll have to **fumigate** the house as it is."

a. Write what you think **fumigate** means in the above sentence.

_____

_____

b. Look up **fumigate** in the dictionary. Write the definition below.

_____

_____

c. Now write how you think the owners would have to **fumigate** the house after "lice and filth and all."

_____

_____

2. Locate paragraph 22 and find the word **rheumatism**.
   (Hint: You won't see many words that begin with *rh*. The *h* is silent.
   The *eu* vowel combination makes the sound of long *u*.)

   a. Look up **rheumatism** in the dictionary. Write the definition below.

   _____

   _____

   b. Write where you think Grandmother could have **rheumatism**.

   _____

   _____

   c. Give your opinion as to why the rain made her **rheumatism** worse.

   _____

   _____

3. Paragraph 28 contains the phrase **truant officer**. Reread paragraphs
   28 and 29.

   a. A police officer and a **truant officer** were both after Frankie.
      You know about police officers. How do you think a **truant
      officer** is different from a police officer?

   _____

   _____

   b. Look up **truant** in the dictionary and see if you were correct.

   _____

   _____

   Now look back at any words that you circled in the story. Could you
   use any of these techniques to figure out what those words mean?

Read with Understanding You have read "Gypsy Life" and have asked yourself questions and looked for *facts* and *opinions*. Remember that facts can be proved. Opinions are what people think or feel. Many times, an opinion will use comparing words. Examples of comparing words are *greatest*, *best*, *most*, *least*, *prettiest*, or *ugliest*.

Below are four sentences about the story. Three of the sentences are facts, and one is an opinion. Choose the sentence that is an *opinion*.

① Gypsy women could get a fortune-telling license at the city hall.

② Doreen's mother had been a dukkerer.

③ Fortune telling is the best way for a gypsy woman to make a living.

④ Doreen had already practiced telling fortunes on Frankie.

Understand by Seeing It A fact and opinion chart can help you determine if a statement is a *fact* or an *opinion*. Here is an example of a fact and opinion chart that could be used for Chapter 1 of *Sarah, Plain and Tall.*

Fact (Can it be proved or checked?)	Opinion (Is it what someone believes, thinks, or feels?)
A Sarah is from Maine.	**D** Anna thought Caleb was homely.
B Caleb and Anna's mother died.	**E** Papa thinks Jack is feisty.
C Papa wrote a letter to Sarah.	**F** Sarah believes that she is not mild-mannered.

Below are six statements from "Gypsy Life." Write the letter of each statement in the correct column of the chart.

Fact (Can it be proved or checked?)	Opinion (Is it what someone believes, thinks, or feels?)

A Doreen is a Gypsy.

B It is fun to sing.

C Schools are all the same.

D Gajos should be nicer to Gypsies.

E Grandmother called herself Madame Sedenia.

F Rheumatism is the worst pain a person could have.

Write to Learn Imagine that you have an opportunity to interview Doreen. How would you change Doreen's *opinion* of Gajos? What *facts* could you share about yourself and your friends or family to change Doreen's opinion of Gajos?

Write a list of facts and then organize them into a paragraph. Remember to only use facts.

My list of facts

A Plan for Fame

- *Novel Excerpt*

Heads Up You are about to read an excerpt from *Bigfoot in New York City?* about a boy named Cody Smith. The title of the excerpt is "A Plan for Fame." What is fame? Write your definition of *fame* in the box below.

Fame is _____

_____

_____

_____

As you read, you will use the skills you have been working on in the previous lessons. Remember to notice details and combine them with what you already know to make *inferences*. Also decide if the details are *facts* (can be proved) or *opinions* (what someone feels). As always, ask yourself *questions* because that is what good readers do. The Think-Along Questions will help guide you.

My Thoughts

A Plan for Fame

from Bigfoot in New York City?

by Dorothy Francis

1   My name is Cody Smith. My friend, Maria Romero, and I deliver The *New York Times* in our apartment building. It's near Central Park. And the building is called The Palace. But it's no palace.

What do you think their building is like?

2   Our delivery service was Maria's idea. She wants to be a reporter someday. I guess selling papers is a good way to start. She usually listens to her radio headphones to catch any late-breaking news.

3   I like the extra money we earn delivering papers. Famous people need cash. And I plan to be famous. CODY SMITH—FAMOUS PERSON.

How do you think Cody plans on becoming famous?

4   One day Maria and I had just finished delivering papers.

5   "Get your wren house, Cody," Maria said. "Let's hang it."

6   "Okay, okay," I told Maria. "Don't be so bossy."

7   Maria gets **uppity** because she's five days closer to being 13 than I am.

What do you think *uppity* means?

She's living with us this summer while her folks are in Italy. Italy is planning a celebration. Maria's folks are helping prepare for it.

They're both engineers. And they're helping stabilize the Leaning Tower of Pisa so tourists can climb it again.

8   Maria's parents are paying Mom to keep Maria. That's a good deal for us. Dad forgets to send support checks—a lot. And we need the money.

What can you infer about Cody's family?

9   Spike Slovnick helped me make the wren house. He and his uncle run the elevator in our building. They both really like birds.

10   I punched the button. The elevator clanged from below. Maria wiped her grimy hands on her shirt because the newsprint wouldn't show. She always wears brown shirts that match her eyes.

11   Maria's dark hair curls, but she has a cowlick. My hair's red. And it lies flat.

12   The elevator stopped. And the door sounded like steelies rolling in a marble bag.

What do you think steelies are?

13   "Good afternoon, kids," Mr. Slovnick said.

14   I raised my chin to look Mr. Slovnick in the eye. He stands so straight he reminds me of an exclamation point. Navy blue suit. Red tie. That's his uniform. Before he retired, he used to teach seventh-grade science in Queens.

15   "What are you two doing today?" Mr. Slovnick asked.

continued

A Plan for Fame continued

My Thoughts

16 "We're going to the park to hang the wren house. Can you come along?" I asked. Mom doesn't let Maria and me go to the park alone.

Why do you think Mom doesn't like them to go to the park alone?

17 Mr. Slovnick looked at his watch. "Sure, I'd like to go. I'll get Spike. It's his turn to tend the elevator."

18 Mr. Slovnick let us out in the lobby. Then he went to his room in the basement. Spike lives down there too.

19 "Where's the wren house?" Maria asked. She looked among the plants in the lobby window.

20 Spike has a small houseplant business here at The Palace. He plant-sits for people on vacation. He's real interested in birds and plants. Mr. Slovnick encourages him a lot.

21 "The wren house isn't here, Cody," Maria said.

22 "I hid it in the vase," I answered. I hurried to the fat orange vase near the window.

23 I hate to hurry in the lobby. Hurrying kicks up dust from the old carpet. It grits on my teeth.

24 Maria flopped onto the couch. Then she popped up again. "Hard! I forgot how hard it is," she said, rubbing her backside. "Nobody sits there except Mrs. Sugarman when she needs to rest."

What can you infer about Mrs. Sugarman?

25   "I saved her life once," I said. "She was doing laundry. Right between rinse and spin, her heart began hurting. She screamed. She couldn't get the cap off her child-safe pill bottle. So I opened it—first try."

26   Maria gave me a half-smile. Sometimes she just humors me. Like she's not really interested. She tries to act so old, so cool. But maybe I'd told her the story before.

27   Just then Mr. Slovnick returned with Spike at the elevator controls. Spike's 17. His T-shirts sag. And his chinos barely reach his ankles. He slouches and frowns a lot. But Maria and I like him. He treats us okay.

28   We sort of envy him too. He's old enough to quit school if he wants to. I like school. But it would be fun to devote my time to finding fame. Spike's still deciding about next fall.

What facts did you learn about Spike?

29   Mr. Slovnick walked with us to the park. People hurried along the sidewalk. Taxis honked. Buses roared by. I tried not to breathe exhaust fumes as we headed toward the park. I hate bad smells.

30   "Not many people here this afternoon," I said. A few kids followed their sitters. A guy played a guitar. But nobody was listening.

31   "Nothing like the Sunday crowds," Maria said.

continued

My Thoughts

My Thoughts

32   I looked for the balloon vendor. But he wasn't in sight. Then I heard clip-clopping. Behind us, a horse pulled a victoria. That's an old-fashioned black carriage. The driver sat up front. He was driving a lady around the park.

33   "Wow!" Maria's eyes grew as round as king-size Life Savers. She was staring at the horse. "An Appaloosa, Cody. Just like on TV." Maria breathed deeply. "I like the smell of horseflesh."

34   I didn't think the smell was so special. Maria tries to impress me with words she learns from crossword puzzles in the newspaper.

What seems to be Cody's opinion of Maria?

35   We found an oak with a low first limb. Rough bark scraped my hands as I pulled myself up. The leaves had a fresh summer smell. But they looked as if they were dying of terminal grime.

36   "Okay, hand me the wren house," I said. Could they hear my voice shake? I wondered. The limb was really high.

37   "Take it easy," Mr. Slovnick said. "What goes up must come down. The law of gravity." He still threw around science lessons whenever he got a chance.

38   Spike had put a special wire on the wren house. I twisted it around a branch. Finished.

39   When I jumped down, my sleeve pulled up. Maria saw my Band-Aid.

40   "Hurt your arm?" Maria asked.

41   I grinned. I was glad she had asked. Secrets are more fun when you share them.

42   "That Band-Aid will make me famous, Maria," I said. "I plan to wear it for 100 days. Nobody else has worn the same Band-Aid a hundred days. When the *Guinness Book of World Records* people hear of it, I'll be famous overnight."

43   "How long have you worn it, Cody?" Mr. Slovnick asked.

44   "One day. So far," I answered.

45   "Why this thing about being famous?" Maria asked.

46   I wasn't about to tell. It hurts to think about it. And Maria wouldn't understand. Her dad will be back in September. Mine won't.

47   Dad never calls or comes to visit. I guess he doesn't like us because I'm such a loser. A zero.

48   But my picture in the *Guinness Book* will grab Dad's attention. Fame makes a person somebody. When I'm famous, Dad will be calling me every day.

What's Cody's opinion of himself?

49   "Cody, I don't think you can do it," Maria said. "Once I tried to chew the same piece of gum for a year. No way. I swallowed it in my sleep. Being famous isn't easy."

50   "I'm not going to give up," I said. "As long as I'm trying, I haven't failed."

continued

A Plan for Fame continued

51   We returned to The Palace. Then we rode to the basement with Mr. Slovnick. Just for the ride. Maria sniffed. The basement always smells of mice and damp concrete. The air smells better on our tenth floor. Spike let us out of the elevator there.

52   It was hot in our apartment. We sat on the fire escape to wait until Mom got home. She's a plainclothes store detective.

What do you think Cody's mom does in her job?

53   But before Mom arrived, we heard Mrs. Sugarman in the hallway. She was sputtering.

54   I unlocked our door and ran to her. Mrs. Sugarman has a flour-sack figure—pudgy. She dyes her gray hair so it's blue. Weird. But it blends with the purple jumpsuit she always wears. She reminds me of a fat violet.

55   "Do you need help with your pill bottle, Mrs. Sugarman?" I asked.

56   She shook her head and gasped, "Cody, call the police!"

Read with Understanding Select the correct answers below for "A Plan for Fame."

1. The best definition of **uppity** as it appears in paragraph 7 is

   Ⓐ "to feel upset."

   Ⓑ "to feel better than."

   Ⓒ "to feel grateful."

   Ⓓ "to feel happy."

2. Which one of the following questions do you think would most likely be answered in the next chapter of *Bigfoot in New York City?*

   Ⓐ How much does Mr. Slovnick make as an elevator operator?

   Ⓑ Why did they choose an oak tree for the wren house?

   Ⓒ Why does the basement smell like mice and damp concrete?

   Ⓓ Why did Mrs. Sugarman want Cody to call the police?

   continued

3. Three of the following statements are facts and one is an opinion. Choose the sentence that is an *opinion*.

   Ⓐ Cody lives on the tenth floor.

   Ⓑ Spike is cool.

   Ⓒ The apartment building is called The Palace.

   Ⓓ The apartment building is near Central Park.

4. What is the main reason Cody feels like a zero?

   Ⓐ Cody feels like his father doesn't like him.

   Ⓑ Maria is older than Cody.

   Ⓒ He hasn't made it into the *Guinness Book* yet.

   Ⓓ Spike knows so much about birds and plants.

Understand by Seeing It Use the information provided by the author and combine it with information you already know to make some *inferences* about life in New York City.

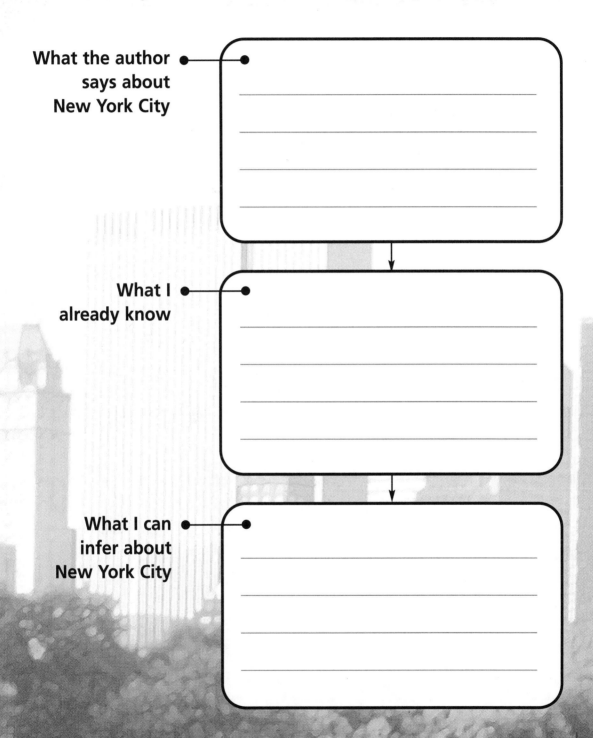

What the author says about New York City

What I already know

What I can infer about New York City

Write to Learn Organize your *inferences* about life in New York City into a paragraph.

School Days

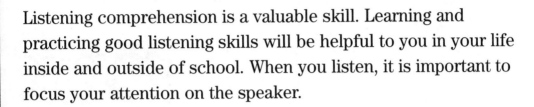

• *Short Story*

Listening comprehension is a valuable skill. Learning and practicing good listening skills will be helpful to you in your life inside and outside of school. When you listen, it is important to focus your attention on the speaker.

Listen as your teacher reads the story "School Days." Your teacher will stop about halfway through and ask you to make a prediction by answering the first question below.

1. Why do you think Mark doesn't want to go to school?

_____

After your teacher finishes reading "School Days," answer the second question below.

2. What was the surprise in the story?

_____

Now your teacher will read "School Days" again. Listen carefully and then answer the question below.

3. What clues did the author use that were misleading?

Lesson 7

Danger
at the Pond

• *Novel Excerpt*

Heads Up You are about to
read an excerpt from the book *The Spy Catchers*. As you
read, you need to be aware of what is happening in the story.
These are called the *events*. Stories must have events. Often, the
events are guided by the *problem*. The problem makes the story
more interesting.

The title of this excerpt is "Danger at the Pond." Predict some
problems the title suggests and list them below.

Possible Problems

Pay attention to events as you read. Answering the Think-Along
Questions should help you focus your thinking. Also, as you read,
circle or highlight any words you don't know.

Danger
at the Pond

from The Spy Catchers

by Dorothy Francis

My Thoughts

1 Brady Ott clenched his fists. Anger boiled over his deep sadness. He hated this war. He would never forget the day his family had received the telegram. It had begun, "We **regret** to inform you—"

2 His brother, Bill, had died at Pearl Harbor. It wasn't fair!

What do you know about what happened at Pearl Harbor?

3 Brady remembered how he and Bill had played ball. Bill had taught him to ice-skate. And Bill had given Brady his snare drum. How could he go on living without Bill?

4 The following Monday after school, Brady looked for Red Johnson. His best friend was an upbeat go-getter. And he was a good listener. Brady counted on Red to always be there for him.

5 "Those dirty Japanese!" Brady said through clenched teeth. "We've got to stop them."

6 "Sure," Red said. "Count me in. But what can two sixth graders do? What's your plan?"

7 "Let's catch spies," Brady said. "That would be a big, important thing to do. Spies told Japan when and where to attack America."

When does this story take place?

8 "Yeah," Red agreed. He lowered his voice. "Spies may be all around us."

continued

Danger at the Pond continued

9   Brady nodded. "We could be in danger right this minute." He looked over his shoulder. But he only saw his classmates.

10   "Come to the pond with me," Brady said. He patted his skates slung over his shoulder. "Go get your skates. We can make secret plans when we get there."

11   "I can't skate today," Red said. "First, I have to do my paper route. Then after supper, I'm helping Dad work on our car. Anyway, see you tomorrow."

12   "See ya," Brady said.

13   Brady hurried to the pond. It was just a few blocks from the school. Hallie Jones was already there, skating alone. She left quickly when she saw Brady.

14   Is she shy? Brady wondered. Or is she just stuck-up?

15   Brady was glad Hallie had left. He needed to be alone. He needed to think about spies—and Bill.

16   Brady wondered why nobody else was skating. The ice looked smooth and strong. He sat on a log and pulled on his skates. The steel blades chilled his fingers.

What event do you think is going to happen?

17   Soon Brady was gliding over the ice. He was thinking about spies when—BANG! The ice popped like a firecracker as it broke. Dark water sloshed over Brady's feet.

18 Down. Down. Brady felt himself falling. He waved his arms. But he couldn't regain his balance.

19 Icy water soaked his clothes. He choked on its fishy taste. His skates were like lead weights. But he fought his way to the surface. He gasped for air.

20 "Help!" Brady yelled. He clutched the jagged ice. It broke off in his hands.

21 "Help!"

22 He tried to pull himself up. But more ice splintered off.

23 "Help! Someone help me."

What is the main problem so far?

24 "Don't panic," a voice called. "I'm right here. And I'll help."

25 The ice cracked again as a girl approached. She quickly backed away.

26 Brady wanted to beg her to stay and help. But he was choking and coughing. He fought to get his breath. He couldn't speak.

27 Soon the girl returned carrying a long stick. She inched along the ice toward Brady.

What do you think she is going to do with the stick?

28 "Hang on," she said. She carefully lay down on her stomach. Holding on to the end of the stick, she pushed it toward Brady.

continued

Danger at the Pond continued

29   "Grab it," she said. "Grab it and hang on. Then try to pull yourself up."

30   Brady grabbed the stick. Slowly he tried to ease onto the ice. But it kept breaking away.

31   "Don't give up," the girl coached. "Try again. You can do it."

32   Brady tried again and again. At last, he pulled himself from the pond. At first, he lay on his stomach, panting and shivering. Then he tried to move.

Do you think the problem has been solved, or will more events happen around this problem? Why?

33   "Easy," the girl warned. She rolled away from him. "Move slowly. I still hear the ice cracking." Brady started to stand. He braced himself with his hands. He bent one knee for support. Water lapped over the jagged edge of the hole.

34   "Wait," the girl said. "Lie flat or the ice will break again. Keep your weight spread over a big area. My dad's a Boy Scout leader. He taught me what to do. Hang on to the stick."

35   Brady lay quietly. He hardly dared to breathe. Lying on her stomach, the girl inched backward. She kept her grip on the stick. Slowly she pulled Brady to stronger ice.

36   Then they both stood. Water streamed from Brady's clothes. It puddled at his feet.

37   "Are you okay?" the girl asked. "You look as pale as milk."

38   "I—I'm okay. Just c—cold and w—wet," Brady said, shivering. "Th—thanks for s—saving me! I don't know wh—what I'd have d—done without you. I m—might have d—died."

Why is Brady talking like that?

He wanted to say more. But he couldn't find the right words. How could he thank someone who saved his life?

Make Sense of Words When you come across an unknown word, you can try to understand the meaning by:

- rereading the sentence and using the *context clues*. This means paying attention to the other words in the sentence and the paragraph.

- breaking the word into parts. A *base word* is the main part of a word. A *prefix* is added to the beginning of a base word to change its meaning. A *suffix* is added to the end of a base word to change its meaning.

- using the dictionary or asking an adult.

1. Find the word **regret** in paragraph 1.

   a. Read the sentences around the word and write what you think **regret** means.

   _____

   _____

   b. Look up **regret** in the dictionary and write the definition.

   _____

   _____

   c. Can you think of a time in your life when you have felt **regret**? Write about that time in the space below.

   _____

   _____

   _____

   _____

Read with Understanding Here are four events from the story. Number them in the order that they happened.

_____ A girl pushed a stick toward Brady.

_____ Brady and Red decided to catch spies.

_____ Brady fell through the ice.

_____ Brady went alone to the pond to think.

Understand by Seeing It A story map can help you identify the important *events*, the *problem*, and the *solution*. Here is an example of a story map for "The Three Little Pigs."

Event 1

Pig number 1 built a house of straw.

↓

Event 2

Pig number 2 built a house of sticks.

↓

Event 3

Pig number 3 built a house of bricks.

Problem	**Solution**
The wolf wanted to eat the pigs. →	The pigs tricked the wolf down the chimney into a boiling pot.

Now create a story map for "Danger at the Pond."

Event 1

Event 2

Event 3

Problem

Solution

Write to Learn The title of this excerpt was "Danger at the Pond." In the Heads Up section, you predicted what the *problem* would be. Then you read to see what really happened. Write a paragraph describing a different plot for the title "Danger at the Pond." Be sure to include a description of *events*, a *problem*, and a *solution*.

Lesson 8

The Ugly Duckling

• *Fairy Tale*

Heads Up "The Ugly Duckling" is a fairy tale written by a famous author, Hans Christian Andersen. Based on the title, what do you think the story is going to be about? Complete the story frame below.

The story takes place _____.

_____ is a character in the story who

_____.

A problem occurs when _____

_____.

The problem is solved when _____

_____.

The story ends with _____

_____.

As you read the tale, think about the important *events* in the story. See if you can identify the *problem* as you read. While you're reading, be sure to ask yourself questions. Answering the Think-Along Questions will help you think about what you're reading. Also, as you read, circle or highlight any words you don't know.

The Ugly Duckling

by Hans Christian Andersen • retold by L. L. Owens

1   It was a clear summer day in the country. A lovely old farmhouse stood in a sunny spot. The house was near a deep river. And near the river sat a duck on her nest. This duck had been waiting and watching for her eggs to hatch. Finally, one shell cracked. Then another. And another.

2   Three tiny creatures lifted their heads and cried, "Peep-peep-peep!"

3   "Quack-quack-quack," said the mother. And then they all quacked as well as they could.

4   The little ones looked about.

5   The mother told her youngsters all about the land and the river. She shared other knowledge with them too.

6   After a while, the mother noticed something. Her largest egg had not yet hatched. So she seated herself on the nest at once.

7   Before long, an old duck stopped by for a visit. She'd heard that the new ducklings had arrived.

8   "How are you feeling?" asked the old duck.

9   "I'm just fine, thank you. But look. This egg doesn't seem to want to hatch."

10   "Oh, yes. I see," said the old duck. "What you have there is a turkey's egg. See how big and gray it is?"

11   "A turkey's egg?" said the duck. "Don't be ridiculous. This is one of my eggs. Trust me, a mother knows."

12   "Whatever you say, dear," said the old duck. She wasn't convinced. But she thought it best to drop the subject. As she waddled away, she muttered, "Too bad turkeys don't like the water."

What kind of egg do you think it will be?

13   At last, the big gray egg broke. The duckling cried, "Peep-peep-peep!"

14   The mother said, "Quack-quack-quaaa—" But she stopped short.

Why did she stop short?

15   The duckling looked up at her with trusting eyes. "Quack-quack-quack," repeated the duckling.

16   The mother was stunned. Not by what she heard—but by what she saw. This duckling was very large. And very ugly.

17   "Well, my goodness!" exclaimed the mother. "What have we here?" She didn't know what else to say. After some thought, she said, "Come and meet the other ducklings."

18   The next day, the mother took her young ones to the water. She jumped in with a splash.

19   "Quack-quack-quack!" the mother cried. And all her little ducklings jumped in.

20   The ducklings bobbed about. Each time their heads disappeared underwater, they popped right back up again. They peeped and quacked with joy at their new adventure. Soon they were all swimming quite gracefully. Especially the ugly duckling.

continued

My Thoughts

My Thoughts

21   "Oh, goody!" cheered the mother. And she called the old duck over to take a look.

22   "See there, old duck," the mother said excitedly. "My youngest duckling cannot be a turkey—he swims so well! And honestly, once you get used to him, he's not so very ugly after all."

23   "If you say so, dear," replied the old duck.

24   "Quack-quack-quack!" called the mother to her **brood**. "Come, children. It is time for you to meet the other animals in the farmyard. I want all of you to be on your best behavior."

What event do you think will happen next?

25   The other ducks stared as the family approached. "Look," said one duck. "Here comes the new brood. They've certainly got a strange brother."

26   "What a funny-looking thing," said a mean duck. "We don't want him here!" And he flew out and bit the ugly duckling's leg.

27   "Ouch!" cried the ugly duckling. "That hurt!"

28   "Leave him alone," warned the mother. "He did nothing to hurt you."

29   "But he is so big. And he's the ugliest duckling ever," retorted the mean duck. "We cannot allow him to stay on this farm."

30   "He is part of my family," said the mother. "And he will stay with me."

31   The ugly duckling was laughed at all day long. The ducks bit him. The chickens pecked at him. And the girl who fed the animals kicked him.

32   When he could take no more, the ugly duckling decided to run away. "No one will miss me!" he sobbed. He flew and flew as far as he could. He didn't stop until he came to a large moor. Then he huddled up next to a rock and slept through the night.

What is the problem in the story?

33   The next morning, a group of wild ducks found him.

34   "You are terribly ugly," said the wild ducks. "But you may stay here for now. Just don't get in our way."

35   "Thank you," said the ugly duckling. For two days and nights, he rested on the moor. On the third day, two wild geese happened by.

36   "Listen, duckling," said one of the geese. "We're flying to another moor today. Would you like to come with us?"

37   "I'd like that. Thank you," replied the duckling.

38   So the little party took off. They had flown just a few hundred yards when they heard an awful racket.

What do you think is going to happen?

continued

My Thoughts

39   *POP! POP! POP! POP! POP!* echoed in the distance. And a whole flock of wild geese rose up from the reeds. They shouted to one another, "Run for your lives!"

40   At that moment, a mean-looking dog rushed toward the duckling. His big pink tongue was wagging. And his eyes were narrowed for the hunt. He gave the duckling a quick sniff and a snort. Then he splashed into the water to fetch an injured goose.

41   "Goodness, me," sighed the duckling. He was relieved, though, that the dog had found him too ugly even to bite.

42   The duckling hid behind a tree for several hours. He didn't dare make a sound. When the shooting and howling died down, he made a decision.

43   "I must go out into the world again," he declared.

44   After a day or so, he came upon a pretty blue lake. He plunged in, eager to swim again. The water was so calm and so warm. And soon the duckling was splashing about.

45   Autumn arrived. And the leaves on the trees turned orange and gold. When the early winds of winter blew the leaves off the trees, the young duckling felt sad.

46   One crisp evening, he sat shivering in his little home of twigs and leaves. At dusk, a flock of beautiful white birds rose from the bushes. The

duckling watched the graceful creatures in wonder. They were swans—with curved necks and silky feathers.

47   The birds cried out as one and spread their splendid wings. They flew away to warm homes across the sea. As they flew higher and higher, the ugly duckling felt a **kinship** with them. He paddled into the water, stretched out his neck, and gave a familiar cry. It sounded just like the cry of the swans!

48   "How I wish I were a swan," said the duckling. He watched and watched until the flock was out of sight.

What do you think the solution to the problem in the story will be?

49   The days grew shorter and colder. Winter raged on. It was a miserable season for the poor duckling.

50   One day, the young bird felt strong enough to fly again. So he flapped his wings and rose high into the sky. He stopped to rest in a large garden. There he saw three white swans swimming in a pond. Cautiously, he dropped into the water and swam to them.

51   The moment the swans saw him, they rushed to his side.

52   The poor bird, fearing an attack, hung his head and waited.

continued

My Thoughts

53   But wait! What did he see in the clear water below? Why, it was his own image. And it was that of a magnificent white swan. He'd grown up over the long, hard winter. And he wasn't a duck—or even a turkey—after all!

54   The other swans greeted the stranger and stroked his neck. "Welcome to our flock!"

55   Presently, some children skipped into the garden. They threw bits of cake into the water.

56   A boy cried, "Come see! There is a new one."

57   The other children were thrilled. And they danced and clapped and sang, "A new swan has arrived!"

58   "The new swan is the most beautiful of all!" said one of the girls.

59   The old swans bowed their heads toward the newcomer. He shyly covered his face with his wing. He was confused. All of his life, he had been hated for his ugliness. And now others said he was the most beautiful bird of all.

60   Then a dazzling beam of sunlight washed over him. The swan realized why he had suffered so. And he was grateful. For it made the joy around him seem that much grander.

61   So he rustled his feathers, curved his slender neck, and cried out to those around him: "Happiness has found me at last! And I shall cherish it forever!"

What is the solution?

Make Sense of Words When you come across an unknown word, you can try to understand the meaning by:

- rereading the sentence and using the *context clues*. This means paying attention to the other words in the sentence and the paragraph.

- breaking the word into parts. A *base word* is the main part of a word. A *prefix* is added to the beginning of a base word to change its meaning. A *suffix* is added to the end of a base word to change its meaning.

- using the dictionary or asking an adult.

1. Look for the word **brood** in paragraph 24. Reread the paragraph. You should be able to tell what this word means from other clues in the paragraph.

   a. Write the clues in the box below.

   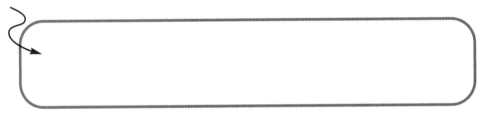

   b. What do you think **brood** means?

   _____

   c. Look up **brood** in the dictionary to see if you were right.

   _____

   d. Now substitute a synonym for the word **brood** in the original sentence:

   " 'Quack-quack-quack!' called the mother

   to her _____."

   (brood)   *continued*

2. In paragraph 47, locate the word **kinship**.

    a. You can break this word into parts. **Kin** is the base word, and **ship** is the suffix.

    b. Look up **kin** in the dictionary, and write the definition on the line under **kin**.

    > **kin**   **+**   **ship**
    >
    > _____   **+**   **the condition**

    c. Write what you think **kinship** means.

    _____

    _____

    d. Write a sentence using **kinship**.

    _____

    _____

Now look back at any words that you circled in the story. Could you use any of these techniques to figure out what those words mean?

Read with Understanding One of the following sentences is not an *event* in the life of the ugly duckling. Choose the event that does *not* belong.

① The ugly duckling hatched into a family of several ducklings.

② A mean duck bit the ugly duckling on the leg.

③ A mean turkey bit the ugly duckling on the wing.

④ A group of wild ducks let the ugly duckling stay with them for a while.

Understand by Seeing It There are many *events* in this tale that helped the ugly duckling solve his *problem*.

What is the ugly duckling's problem?

_____

_____

Now go back to the story and choose three events that helped the ugly duckling with his problem. Be sure to put the events in sequence (the order they happened in the tale). Illustrate each event. Then describe the event on the lines below your illustration.

Event 1

_____

_____

Event 2

Event 3

_____

_____

Write to Learn Think of two more *events* you would like to happen to the ugly duckling after he discovers his true identity. Use these events to write a paragraph that tells about the ugly duckling's life after this tale ends.

Lesson 9

Rebecca:
Calvin Coolidge's Raccoon

• *Narrative Nonfiction*

Heads Up While you are reading "Rebecca: Calvin Coolidge's Raccoon," you will be focusing on the main character, President Calvin Coolidge. A good author helps you get to know the characters of the story. This is called *characterization*. The author may tell you how the characters look, act, or feel and what others think about them. To practice characterization, make a character diagram of yourself on the next page. On each of the spokes, put a phrase about how you look, act, or feel.

continued

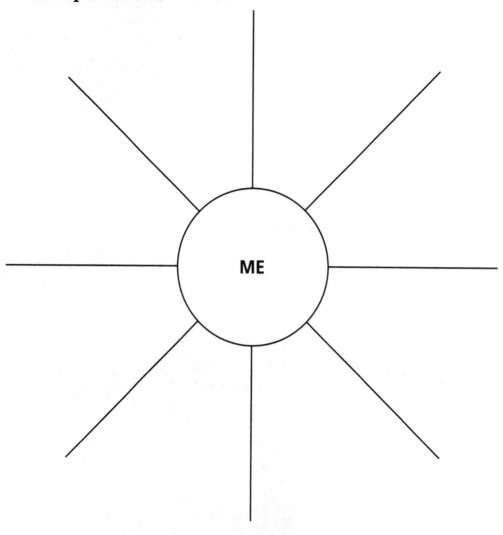

The author of this story will tell you many things about President
Coolidge. You will even know what others think of him. While you
are reading, focus on *characterization* and ask yourself questions.
That is what good readers do. The Think-Along Questions will help
you read actively. Also, as you read, circle or highlight any words you
don't know.

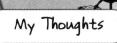

Rebecca:
Calvin Coolidge's Raccoon

by Kathleen Muldoon

1   Calvin Coolidge was the thirtieth president of the United States. Some people thought he was shy. That's because he did not talk or smile very much. People nicknamed him Silent Cal.

2   But President Coolidge was not shy around animals. He and his family probably had more animals than any other first family.

> **Why do you think President Coolidge wasn't shy around animals?**

3   Coolidge had several dogs. Rob Roy, a white collie, was his favorite. Mrs. Coolidge often dressed their dogs in dresses and hats.

4   President Coolidge also had cats. He liked Tiger best. Tiger was a stray that just showed up one day at the White House. He liked riding up and down on the White House elevator.

5   The Coolidges also had a **mynah bird** and two canaries, Nip and Tuck.

6   People around the world knew of the president's love of animals. They sent him a baby bear and two lion cubs. He also received a hippo, a bobcat, and an antelope. Coolidge gave these big animals to zoos.

> **Describe President Coolidge's character from what you've read so far.**

continued

My Thoughts

7   But one day, he received a special gift from some friends in Mississippi. They sent him a furry raccoon. The president named her Rebecca. She became his favorite pet of all.

Why do you suppose Rebecca was his favorite pet?

8   Rebecca was allowed to **roam** free. Sometimes visitors thought a wild animal had sneaked into the White House. They were surprised to learn that the raccoon was the president's pet!

9   At night, Rebecca slept outside. The president had a little house built just for her.

10   When he had time, Coolidge took Rebecca on walks. He kept her on a leash. Even on his busiest days, the president found time for Rebecca.

What does this say about President Coolidge's character?

11   Rebecca loved playing in water. Coolidge made sure she always had water in her pen. He liked watching her splash. Sometimes he gave her a bar of soap. Rebecca played and made soapsuds.

12   Once President Coolidge and his family had to move from the White House. Workers needed to make some repairs. The animals stayed in their outside pens and houses.

13   But Coolidge worried about Rebecca. He was afraid she would be lonely without him. She was used to her daily walks and playtime. He

also worried that she might not have enough soap to make suds. The president could not rest. Finally, he called his driver and went to the White House. The president got out and went to Rebecca's pen. He picked her up and brought her to the car.

14   Coolidge took Rebecca to the zoo. He left her there to play with other raccoons until they could be together again at the White House.

15   When they moved back, Coolidge bought another raccoon. He named him Horace. But Rebecca did not like Horace. And Horace did not like Rebecca.

16   One night Horace ran away. That was all right with Rebecca. She liked being the only raccoon in the White House.

From what you know about President Coolidge's character, how do you think he reacted to Horace's running away?

Unit 5: Understand Characterization | *111*

Make Sense of Words When you come across an unknown word, you can try to understand the meaning by:

- rereading the sentence and using the *context clues*. This means paying attention to the other words in the sentence and the paragraph.

- breaking the word into parts. A *base word* is the main part of a word. A *prefix* is added to the beginning of a base word to change its meaning. A *suffix* is added to the end of a base word to change its meaning.

- using the dictionary or asking an adult.

1. In paragraph 5, locate the phrase **mynah bird**.

   a. Look up **mynah bird** in the dictionary. Write the definition.

   _____

   _____

   b. Draw a picture of a **mynah bird** and write a sentence about it.

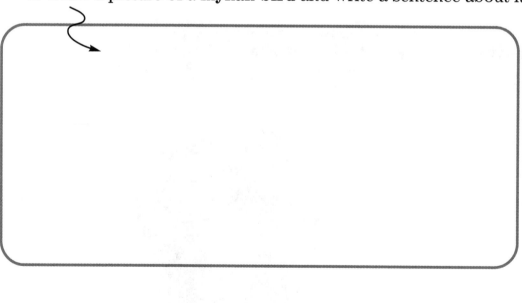

   _____

   _____

2. In paragraph 8, find the word **roam**.

    a. "Rebecca was allowed to **roam** free." What do you think **roam** means in this sentence?

    _____

    _____

    b. Look up **roam** in the dictionary and write the definition.

    _____

    _____

    c. Make a list of synonyms for **roam**. Remember, synonyms are words with the same or nearly the same meaning.

    My Synonyms for Roam

    d. Fill in the blank below with a synonym for **roam**.

    "Rebecca was allowed to _____ free."
                             (roam)

Now look back at any words that you circled in the story. Could you use any of these techniques to figure out what those words mean?

As you read
"Rebecca: Calvin Coolidge's Raccoon," you should have
noticed the many ways the author described President
Coolidge. Sometimes authors describe how a character
looks, acts, or feels. Many times you are also told how
others feel about the character.

Below are four sentences from the story. Underline the
sentence that describes how President Coolidge *acted*.

① President Coolidge was afraid Rebecca would be
lonely without him.

② Rebecca loved playing in water.

③ President Coolidge gave these big animals to zoos.

④ Some people thought President Coolidge was shy.

Understand by Seeing It To help you better understand President Coolidge's *character*, create a character diagram for him. It will be like the one you created for yourself in the Heads Up section. Write statements about what President Coolidge did, felt, and thought in the story. You can even include what others said about him.

Write to Learn Write a paragraph about Calvin Coolidge as a boy. Use your character diagram of President Coolidge and your imagination.

Lesson 10

TEACHER'S PET

from **Marvin Redpost: Alone in His Teacher's House**

• *Novel Excerpt*

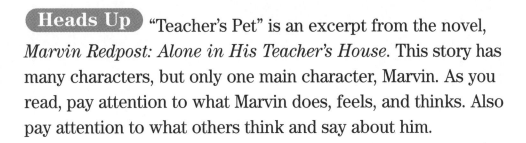

Heads Up "Teacher's Pet" is an excerpt from the novel, *Marvin Redpost: Alone in His Teacher's House.* This story has many characters, but only one main character, Marvin. As you read, pay attention to what Marvin does, feels, and thinks. Also pay attention to what others think and say about him.

Practice *characterization.* Choose a favorite character from a book, movie, or cartoon. On the next page, draw your character and label it with your character's name. Surrounding the picture of your character, write several statements about how your character looks, feels, thinks, acts, or what others may think of the character.

continued

My Favorite Character

Pay attention to the Think-Along Questions as you read. Answering them will help you focus on *characterization*. Also, as you read, circle or highlight any words you don't know.

TEACHER'S PET

from Marvin Redpost:
Alone in His Teacher's House

by Louis Sachar

My Thoughts

1   "You will have a substitute teacher tomorrow," Mrs. North told her third-grade class.

2   "All right!" shouted Nick.

3   Mrs. North stared at Nick.

4   Marvin Redpost looked down at his desk and smiled. Nick Tuffle was Marvin's best friend. Marvin had two best friends. His other best friend was Stuart Albright.

5   "I will be gone for one week," said Mrs. North. "I won't be back until next Thursday. A week from tomorrow."

6   "Hot dog!" exclaimed Nick.

7   Mrs. North glared at Nick. "I will leave detailed instructions for the substitute," she warned. "And if any of you **misbehave**, I will know about it. That means you, Nick."

8   "Hey, why pick on me?" asked Nick.

9   When it was time to go home, Nick and Stuart gathered around Marvin's desk.

10   "A substitute for a week!" said Nick, rubbing his hands together. "This is going to be great."

> Why does Nick think having a substitute for a week will be great?

continued

My Thoughts

11   "Let's pretend we're each other," said Stuart. "I'll be Marvin. Marvin, you be Nick. And Nick, you can be me."

12   "I don't want to be *you*," Nick said to Stuart. "I'll be Marvin, and you be me."

13   "I don't want to be *you!*" said Stuart.

14   It made Marvin feel proud that both his friends wanted to be him.

15   On the other hand, he wasn't sure he wanted either of them to be him.

What does this say about Marvin's character?

16   "Marvin, may I talk to you for a moment?" asked Mrs. North.

17   "What'd you do?" asked Stuart.

18   Marvin shrugged. He didn't think he did anything.

19   And even if he did, what could Mrs. North do about it? She was going away for a week.

20   He walked to her desk.

Why do you think Mrs. North wants to see Marvin?

21   "Do you like dogs?" asked Mrs. North.

22   "Sure," he said.

23   "I'm going to need someone to take care of Waldo while I'm away," said Mrs. North.

24   "Waldo?" asked Marvin.

25   "I was going to put him in a **kennel**," said Mrs. North. "But he's such an old dog. It would be so much nicer if he could stay home."

26   Marvin could hardly believe his ears.

27   "I'll pay you three dollars a day," said Mrs. North. "Times seven days. That's twenty-one dollars. Tell you what. I'll give you a four dollar bonus if there are no problems. Twenty-five dollars."

28   Marvin nodded his head. He was too shocked to speak.

29   "Good," said Mrs. North. "You want to come to my house now and meet Waldo?"

30   Marvin stared at her. "Okay," he said.

31   "I'll call your mother," said Mrs. North. "And I've got a few things to finish up. I'll meet you in the parking lot in twenty minutes."

Why do you think Mrs. North chose Marvin for this job?

32   "Okay."

33   Stuart and Nick were waiting outside for him.

34   "Did you get in trouble?" asked Nick.

35   "No," said Marvin, still in shock.

36   "You want to play soccer?" asked Stuart.

37   "I can't," said Marvin. "I have to meet Mrs. North in the parking lot. She's going to drive me in her car."

38   "*Her car!*" said Nick.

39   "To her house," said Marvin.

40   "*Her house!*" said Stuart.

41   "She's going to pay me to take care of her dog while she's away."

42   His friends stared at him wide-eyed.

continued

My Thoughts

Teacher's Pet continued

43   "Three dollars a day. Plus a bonus of four dollars if there are no problems."

44   "Twenty-five bucks," said Stuart. He was good at math.

45   "You are *so* lucky," said Nick. "You're the luckiest kid in the whole world."

46   Marvin's friends waited with him in the parking lot.

47   "Which one do you think is her car?" asked Stuart.

48   "I don't know," said Marvin.

49   "I can't believe you guys are so dumb!" said Nick. "She drives that yellow Firebird. Over there, next to Mrs. Grant's red Cougar. The pick-up truck is Mr. McCabe's. The van is Mr. Gurdy's. I can tell you every teacher's car."

Why do you think Nick knows everyone's cars?

50   "But you've never driven in one," said Stuart, patting Marvin on the back.

51   Mrs. North came out of the office. She held a folder filled with papers.

52   "Are you ready, Marvin?" she asked.

53   He nodded.

54   "We just wanted to watch him get into your car," said Stuart.

55   Mrs. North smiled. "Well, it's that yellow one, over there."

56   "*I know*," said Nick.

57   Mrs. North and Marvin walked across the parking lot.

58   "May I carry that for you?" Marvin asked.

59   "Thank you, Marvin," said Mrs. North. She handed him the folder. "It's my homework," she told him.

60   "*You* have homework?"

61   "Sure. I have to correct *your* homework. In fact, I have a lot more homework than you. I have to correct your homework, plus the homework of every student in the class."

62   "Hmm," said Marvin. He never thought of that before.

63   She unlocked the door of her car, got in, then reached over and unlocked Marvin's door.

64   He sat down next to her.

65   "You have a very nice car," he said.

66   "Thank you," said Mrs. North.

67   "The seat is very comfortable."

68   "I'm glad you like it," said Mrs. North.

69   He tugged gently on the seat belt. "The seat belt seems nice and strong," he said.

70   "Good," said Mrs. North. "In case I crash." She started the engine. They drove off.

71   Marvin waved out the window to his two best friends. Then he leaned back and enjoyed the ride.

What do you know about Marvin's character?

Make Sense of Words When you come across an unknown word, you can try to understand the meaning by:

- rereading the sentence and using the *context clues*. This means paying attention to the other words in the sentence and the paragraph.

- breaking the word into parts. A *base word* is the main part of a word. A *prefix* is added to the beginning of a base word to change its meaning. A *suffix* is added to the end of a base word to change its meaning.

- using the dictionary or asking an adult.

1. Locate the word **misbehave** in paragraph 7.

   a. The word **misbehave** has a prefix. Look up the word **behave** in the dictionary and write the definition in the "base word" column in the chart below.

prefix	base word
mis	behave
Meaning → opposite of, not	

   b. Use **misbehave** in a sentence.

   _____

   _____

2. In paragraph 25, find the word **kennel**.

   a. By reading the sentence "I was going to put him in a **kennel**," you know that a **kennel** is a place.

b. Look up **kennel** in the dictionary and write the definition.

_____

_____

c. Draw a picture of Waldo in a **kennel** and write a sentence about it.

_____

_____

Now look back at any words that you circled in the story. Could you use any of these techniques to figure out what those words mean?

Read with Understanding You have been thinking about Marvin's character. You should know what he thinks, how he acts, and what others think of him. Read the four sentences below. Choose the sentence that would *not* be true of the main character, Marvin.

① Marvin is responsible.

② Marvin has trouble with school.

③ Marvin is popular with the other students.

④ Marvin is polite.

Understand by Seeing It Another way to help understand a character is to create a character map. Here is an example of a character map for Caleb from *Sarah, Plain and Tall*.

The four statements describe Caleb—what he feels, what he thinks, or how he acts. Under the figure is a sentence about what kind of person Caleb is.

Caleb

He is curious.

He wants to sing the old songs.

He likes the story of his birth.

He wants to remember Mama.

Caleb is a loving, happy little boy.

continued

Here is a simple stick figure representing Marvin. On the four shorter lines, write statements about how Marvin feels, how he thinks, or how he acts. You can also include what others think of him. On the long line, write a sentence about what kind of person Marvin is.

Marvin

Write to Learn After creating your character map, you should have a good understanding of Marvin's *character*. Write a few sentences about Marvin and Waldo's adventures while Mrs. North is gone. Make sure you stay true to Marvin's character in the book.

Lesson 11

The Country Mouse and the Town Mouse

• *Fable*

Heads Up You are about to read a fable written by Aesop, an ancient author. As you read this fable, see if you can figure out (infer) the lesson that Aesop was trying to teach. The general lesson of a story is called the *theme*. You can discover the *theme* by paying close attention to the characters and the events. Some stories have more than one theme. Before you begin reading, think about the difference between living in the country and living in town. Write down two good things about living in the country and two good things about living in town.

Country

_____

_____

Town

_____

_____

Answering the Think-Along Questions will help you focus on what you are reading. Also, as you read, circle or highlight any words you don't know.

The Country Mouse and the Town Mouse

by Aesop • retold by Karen Berg Douglas

1   Once upon a time, if you looked very close, you could see it. It was a tiny hole in the stones of a wall. This was where Country Mouse and his wife lived.

2   They were very happy. Every fall, they went into the fields and picked wheat. Sometimes, they got berries from the bushes. Or acorns from the oak tree. They thought they lived like a king and a queen.

Why did they think they lived like a king and a queen?

3   One day while eating breakfast, they began to think about Town Mouse.

4   "You know, I think we should invite him for a visit," said Country Mouse. "He might like to see how well we live."

5   "You are right," said the wife. "Let's ask him to come this week."

6   A few days later, Town Mouse arrived at their door.

7   "Do come in," said Country Mouse. "We are so happy to see you!"

8   Country Mouse showed Town Mouse his home. He showed off his children. Then he went to the cupboard. He brought out the berries and acorns and wheat.

continued

My Thoughts

The Country Mouse and the Town Mouse continued

9   His wife brought out some crab apples and sweet, white nuts.

10   "Eat, eat! As much as you want!" said Country Mouse.

11   Town Mouse looked down his whiskers. "Is this all you have?" he asked, with a shake of his tail.

How do you think Country Mouse and Mrs. Country Mouse will react to Town Mouse's question?

12   "This is very good food!" said Mrs. Country Mouse. "My husband worked hard to get it. Why, I'm sure no mouse in the world has a cupboard as full as mine!"

13   "Dear lady," said Town Mouse. "This may be all right for the country. But in town, we eat even better!"

14   Mrs. Country Mouse was angry. She took all the food from the table. "Well, then. We will eat this another day," she said.

15   But her husband wanted to know more.

Why did Country Mouse want to know more?

16   "Tell me, how do you live?" asked Country Mouse.

17   "You must visit me and find out," said Town Mouse.

18   So a few days later, Country Mouse brushed his fur and washed his feet and tail. And he started off for the city. Town Mouse met him in the field.

19   "Now, be careful, my dear cousin," said Town Mouse. "When you're in the city, you can't let anyone see you. And you have to be very quiet."

20   So the two mice **crept** into the big house where Town Mouse lived.

21   It was a beautiful house with warm rugs on the floor. There was nice furniture to climb. In the dining room was one tiny hole in the wall. That was where Town Mouse lived.

22   "I think they are getting ready to serve a big dinner," said Town Mouse. "Before I show you my house, let's get something to eat."

23   With that, the two mice climbed up the white lace tablecloth onto the big table. Oh, such fine food they saw!

24   There was ham. And potatoes. There were peas and carrots and fresh wheat rolls. Why, there was even a big round of cheese!

25   "What do you think of this?" said Town Mouse.

26   "Oh, my," Country Mouse replied. "I don't know where to begin!"

27   "Try that ham," said Town Mouse.

28   Country Mouse ran to the other side of the table. But just as he put his tiny foot on the plate, the door to the kitchen opened! In came many happy, hungry people!

29   With a squeak, Town Mouse ran down the tablecloth and into the hole. Country Mouse followed him.

continued

My Thoughts

The Country Mouse and the Town Mouse continued

30   "Whew! I haven't run that fast in a long time," said Country Mouse.

> Why hasn't Country Mouse run that fast for a long time?

31   "Shhhh. Be very quiet now," said Town Mouse. "If they know we are here, they will kill us."

32   The two mice peeked out the hole. They watched the happy people eat up most of the good food.

33   "Don't worry, dear cousin," said Town Mouse. "They will leave some for us."

34   Finally, the people stopped eating. They went to another room to talk. So the two mice crept out of the hole and ran up the tablecloth onto the table again.

35   They had just started to take some ham when the door opened!

36   In came a servant with two big dogs. "Mice! Mice!" he shouted. "We have mice!"

37   The two dogs began to bark. The mice ran across the table, down the lace tablecloth, and into the hole.

38   "Whew! We made it," said Town Mouse.

39   "But I'm still hungry," Country Mouse replied. "Fine food is nice, dear cousin. But if you can't eat it, what use is it? I'm going home."

40   "Well then, be gone with you," said Town Mouse.

> Why was Town Mouse upset?

My Thoughts

41   And with a shake of his tail, Country Mouse was gone.

42   "My family and I will stay where we are," he said happily. As he ran down the road, he added, "We will eat wheat and berries and acorns every day. And no one will get after us!"

43   No one knows what happened to Town Mouse. But Country Mouse and his family lived happily ever after. And they never went back to the city again.

Why didn't they ever go back to the city?

My Thoughts

Make Sense of Words When you come across an unknown word, you can try to understand the meaning by:

- rereading the sentence and using the *context clues*. This means paying attention to the other words in the sentence and the paragraph.

- breaking the word into parts. A *base word* is the main part of a word. A *prefix* is added to the beginning of a base word to change its meaning. A *suffix* is added to the end of a base word to change its meaning.

- using the dictionary or asking an adult.

1. In paragraph 20, find the word **crept**.

   a. The definition of **crept** is "the past tense of **creep**." Look up **creep** in the dictionary and write the definition.

   _____

   _____

   b. Draw a picture of Country Mouse and Town Mouse as they **crept** along. Write a sentence about your picture.

   _____

   _____

   Now look back at any words that you circled in the story. Could you use any of these techniques to figure out what those words mean?

Read with Understanding   As you read "The Country Mouse and the Town Mouse," you focused on the *theme*, or the lesson the author was teaching. Themes are usually general enough that people can use them in their own lives. Below are four themes. Choose which could be a theme of "The Country Mouse and the Town Mouse."

① The best food is served on lace tablecloths.

② You don't have to be so quiet in the country.

③ Always beware of dogs.

④ You should be happy with what you have.

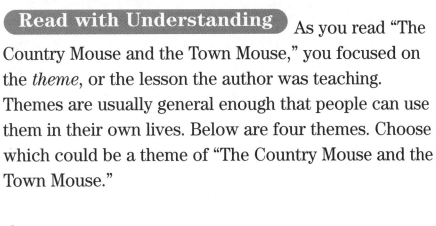

Understand by Seeing It In this fable, Aesop compared the life of a country mouse with the life of a town mouse. Go back through the story. List some good and bad points of living in the country and in town. Then in your own words, write a *theme* that Aesop was trying to teach through the fable.

Country

Good	Bad
_____	_____
_____	_____
_____	_____

Town

Good	Bad
_____	_____
_____	_____
_____	_____

Aesop's theme

© Perfection Learning® No reproduction permitted.

Write to Learn   As you can see, teaching a *theme* by weaving it into a story is clever. Below are several themes. Choose one theme. Write the main points of a fable you could write to teach the theme.

- It's better to be smart than pretty.
- Don't be lazy.
- You should be kind to everyone.
- It's better to be happy than rich.

Main Points

Lesson 12

The Duck and the Moon

• *Poem*

Heads Up The *theme* is a general lesson an author tries to teach to his or her readers. Authors can use many forms of literature, including poetry, to teach *theme*. Benjamin Franklin used his book *Poor Richard's Almanac* to teach themes. Here are some lines from *Poor Richard's Almanac*. Read them and decide what you think Benjamin Franklin's *theme* was for each.

A bird in the hand is worth two in the bush.

_____

A penny saved is a penny earned.

_____

Early to bed, early to rise, makes a man healthy, wealthy, and wise.

_____

You will be reading a poem. Answer the Think-Along Questions to focus on the *theme* of the poem. Also, as you read, circle or highlight any words you don't know.

The Duck and the Moon

by Leo Tolstoy

1 A duck was once swimming along the river
2 looking for fish.

> Why was the duck looking for fish?

3 The whole day passed
4 without her finding a single one.
5   When night came
6 she saw the moon reflected on the water,
7 and thinking it was a fish
8 she dived down to catch it.

> Why did she think the moon was a fish?

9 The other ducks saw her,
10 and they all made fun of her.

> Why did the other ducks think this was so funny?

11   From that day
12 the duck was so ashamed and so **timid**,
13 that even when she did see a fish under water
14 she would not try to catch it,
15 and before long she died of hunger.

> Why wouldn't she dive when she was starving?

Make Sense of Words When you come across an unknown word, you can try to understand the meaning by:

- rereading the sentence and using the *context clues*. This means paying attention to the other words in the sentence and the paragraph.

- breaking the word into parts. A *base word* is the main part of a word. A *prefix* is added to the beginning of a base word to change its meaning. A *suffix* is added to the end of a base word to change its meaning.

- using the dictionary or asking an adult.

1. In line 12, locate the word **timid**. This word is important in understanding the meaning of the poem.

   a. Look up **timid** in the dictionary and write the definition.

   _____

   _____

   b. Fill in the blank below with a synonym for **timid**.

      "From that day the duck was so ashamed and so

      _____, that even when she did see a fish
            (timid)

      under water she would not try to catch it, and before long she died of hunger."

Now look back at any words that you circled in the story. Could you use any of these techniques to figure out what those words mean?

Read with Understanding Below are four sentences about "The Duck and the Moon." Select the one you feel could be a *theme* of this poem.

① Don't be concerned about what others think of you.

② You should always try to get the fish first.

③ It's good to make fun of others.

④ Being ashamed and timid will keep you from eating.

Understand by Seeing It Reread the poem. Make notes in the duck below about what the author tells you about the duck in the poem. In your own words, write a *theme* that the author was trying to teach. Write your theme on the lines under the duck.

Write to Learn Look at the *theme* you chose in
Read with Understanding. Do you agree with this theme?
Write a paragraph explaining your answer.

Johnny Appleseed

• *American Folktale*

Heads Up You are about to read a famous American folktale about Johnny Appleseed. As you read, remember the skills of analyzing the *plot* and the *characters*. You worked on these skills in previous lessons. There are also several *themes* taught by Johnny Appleseed. See if you can identify them.

Before you read, think about Johnny Appleseed. Have you heard of him? What do you know? What do you want to find out? Fill in the first two sections of the KWL chart below and on the next page about Johnny Appleseed. You will fill out the **L** section for what you have learned after you read.

K

(What do I Know about Johnny Appleseed?)

_____

_____

_____

_____

_____

W
(What do I Want to know about Johnny Appleseed?)

_____

_____

_____

_____

_____

L
(What did I Learn about Johnny Appleseed?)

_____

_____

_____

_____

_____

As always, answer the Think-Along Questions, which will help you be an active reader.

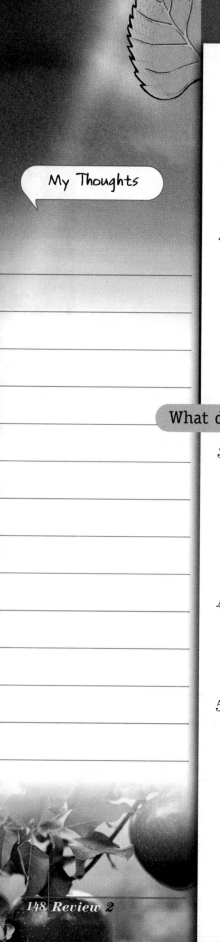

Johnny Appleseed

retold by Peg Hall

My Thoughts

1   There were two things young John Chapman loved. One was animals. The other was apple trees.

2   John was born in Boston on a wild and rainy spring day. Some tell a story about his birth. They say that as soon as Johnny took his first breath, the storm stopped. The sun came out and splashed a rainbow across the sky. That rainbow ended right at the door of the Chapman house.

What do you think this says about Johnny's character?

3   No one knows whether or not that story's true. But right from the start, it was clear that the boy was special. He had some kind of magic to him. Wild animals would come right out of the forest to visit him. Sick and hurt creatures would heal at Johnny's touch.

4   But it wasn't just the animals that felt Johnny's magic. Plants did too. In fact, anything that Johnny stuck in the dirt soon grew tall and strong.

5   Maybe that gift is what got Johnny started planting apple seeds. Or maybe it was the **notion** that there wasn't anything better than apple trees and that there shouldn't be any place where they didn't grow.

6   Whatever the reason, it's a good thing Johnny did what he did. Without him, there might not be any apples west of the great Mississippi River.

My Thoughts

7   You see, Johnny lived during an itchy time. People were on the move from east to west. It seemed like every day another family packed up and headed off. They went to find new land and new dreams. They went to seek adventure and riches. They went just to see what was out there.

8   And sometimes one or two would come back. They'd tell tales of all the things they had seen.

9   One day when Johnny was just about grown, he met a man who changed his life. Johnny was hard at work in the family orchard. He was happily picking apples when the man came by.

10   "I'd give a lot for one of them apples, boy," the man called.

11   Johnny laughed and tossed an apple to the man. "You can have it for nothing," he said.

What does this action tell you about Johnny's character?

12   The man stopped to eat the apple. In between bites, he told his story. He had been out to the West. Now he was back to get his family. They were going to settle out there.

13   "It's a great place, son," said the man. "Though I sure do miss apples. You don't see any apple trees out there."

continued

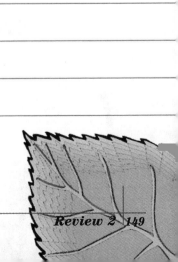

Johnny Appleseed continued

14   "Well, then," said Johnny. "Take some seeds with you. Plant them and you'll soon have your own apples."

15   "That's a fine thought," said the man. "I'll do it."

16   That gave Johnny an idea. He could give apple seeds to people who were headed to the West. If they each planted a few seeds, soon orchards would bloom there. There would be apples for everyone.

17   So that's what Johnny started doing. He collected seeds from apples that fell on the ground. He went through the mash left after making cider and picked out the seeds. Before long he had a leather bag filled with seeds.

18   Of course, people thought he was a bit crazy. The boy talked to animals, after all. And he picked up seeds everywhere he went. What else could people think?

Were people right? Do you think Johnny was crazy?

19   None of that bothered Johnny. He didn't care what other people thought. He only cared about two things. One was animals. The other was apple trees.

Can you figure out a theme from paragraph 19?

20   But after a while, Johnny began to think he wasn't doing enough. He didn't know if anyone actually planted the seeds he sent west with them. The only way he could be sure was to plant them himself.

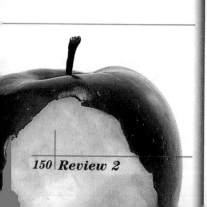

21   So Johnny outfitted himself for the West. He was a simple man, so he didn't need much. He put a beat-up, old pot on his head to keep off the hot sun. He made a traveling suit by cutting holes in an old feed sack. Then he put his bag of seeds over one shoulder and set out.

22   Johnny walked the whole way. (Except when he had to cross the Ohio River.) He walked for hundreds and hundreds of miles. Most of the time, he was barefoot. It didn't matter if it rained or snowed. Johnny didn't mind.

23   As he traveled, Johnny handed out apple seeds. He told people to plant them.

24   Every so often, Johnny would settle somewhere for a spell. That was whenever someone gave him a piece of land to use. Then Johnny would plant seeds himself. He'd start a new orchard and gather a new supply of seeds. Soon there were apple trees all over Ohio and Indiana.

25   It was hard work, but Johnny was happy. He became known far and wide as "Johnny Appleseed." Stories about him were heard everywhere.

26   One of those stories was about Johnny and some bugs. It seems that one night Johnny made a fire. But before long, he noticed little sparks blazing up and falling into the flames. He saw that the sparks were bugs. The creatures were drawn to the flames. But when they got close, the heat set their wings on fire.

continued

Johnny Appleseed continued

27   Well, Johnny wasn't about to let that happen. Even to a bug. So right away he put that fire out. He slept in the cold that night and every night afterward.

28   Another time Johnny crawled into a big hollow log to sleep. As he went in, he heard a snort and a grumble. There was a big brown bear in the log!

29   That didn't bother Johnny, of course. He just said, "Excuse me, Brother Bear." The surprise is that it didn't seem to bother the bear either. The two of them just cuddled up for the night inside that log.

What do these events say about Johnny's character?

30   But best of all is the story about Johnny and the wolf. It seems that one day Johnny was picking herbs. He heard a low howl just ahead.

31   It was a sad howl, the howl of an animal in trouble. So Johnny had to go look. He found a great black wolf with its paw stuck in a steel trap.

32   Another man might have shot that wolf. Another man might just have left quietly the way he came. But not Johnny. He walked right up to the wolf. Without a care for himself, he reached down and pulled off the trap. Then he wrapped a cloth around the hurt paw.

33   From then on, Johnny and the wolf were always together. When Johnny set out to walk,

the wolf followed. When Johnny lay down to sleep, the wolf curled up next to him. Some even say the wolf would use its paws to dig holes for Johnny's seeds.

me up with from this event?

34   The two of them traveled all over this great country. They traveled all the way to the Rocky Mountains. And in each place they stopped, an apple orchard would later spring up.

35   Johnny and the wolf went on this way for years. After a while, Johnny's hair turned gray, and his step slowed a bit. The wolf's fur grew gray, and its eyes dimmed. Still they walked on.

36   Until one day, a farmer saw the wolf. The man hadn't heard about Johnny and his wolf. Quick as a flash, he raised his rifle. Quick as a flash, he shot that wolf.

37   Johnny was heartbroken. He sat for a long time beside his dead friend. At last he buried the wolf by the side of a stream. He planted his best apple seeds at the edges of the grave. No one is sure where the spot is now. But some say the apple trees grow thicker there than anywhere else.

38   After that, Johnny went on alone. He missed the wolf, but he was happy in his work. Everywhere he went, orchards sprang up.

39   "That Johnny Appleseed," people would say. "He's crazy!"

continued

© Perfection Learning® No reproduction permitted.

My Thoughts

40   Johnny didn't care. He just walked on. Until finally the day came when he was too tired to walk anymore.

41   Johnny lay down in a small orchard. He looked up at the branches overhead. Then he closed his eyes. His work was done.

42   The next day, a traveler found Johnny's body. Around him was a quiet circle of animals.

Why were the animals sitting around Johnny's body?

43   Johnny was buried in that orchard. But his work lives on in every apple seed that gets planted. In every apple tree that blossoms and bears fruit. And in every crisp apple that gets eaten.

Read with Understanding Thinking about "Johnny Appleseed," select the best answer for each question.

1. In paragraph 5, which could *not* be a definition of **notion**?
   Ⓐ fact
   Ⓑ idea
   Ⓒ belief
   Ⓓ feeling

2. Which sentence could *not* be a theme of "Johnny Appleseed"?
   Ⓐ Be kind to animals.
   Ⓑ It's better to give than to receive.
   Ⓒ It's better to be rich than poor.
   Ⓓ Follow your own dreams.

3. In paragraph 7, it states Johnny lived during an "itchy" time. Reread the rest of the paragraph. Why was this called an "itchy" time?
   Ⓐ Long underwear made people itch.
   Ⓑ The cold weather caused dry skin.
   Ⓒ It was an area with a lot of bugs.
   Ⓓ People were wanting to move west.

continued

4. Which of these would *not* be a statement about the kind of person Johnny Appleseed was?

   Ⓐ He was caring.

   Ⓑ He was generous.

   Ⓒ He was selfish.

   Ⓓ He was persistent.

5. Put these events in the order they happened in this folktale.

   _____ The wolf accompanied Johnny Appleseed on his travels.

   _____ The rainbow ended at the Chapman house the day Johnny was born.

   _____ Animals surrounded Johnny's body in the orchard.

   _____ Johnny decided to go west and plant apple seeds.

Understand by Seeing It Create a story map for "Johnny Appleseed." The problem has been filled in for you. Find two *events* in Johnny's story that helped him identify his problem. Also write how Johnny solved his problem.

Event 1

Event 2

Problem

More apple trees were needed in the world.

Solution

Write to Learn Pretend that you are a newspaper reporter during the time of Johnny Appleseed's life. You have been assigned to write an article about his life and death. Include what kind of person Johnny Appleseed was, the important events in his life, and what people should learn from him now that he is gone.

_____

_____

_____

_____

_____

_____

_____

_____

_____

_____

_____

_____

_____

The Three of Them

• *Short Story*

Listening comprehension is a valuable skill. Learning and practicing good listening skills will be helpful to you in your life inside and outside of school. When you listen, it is important to sit quietly and focus your attention on the speaker.

Listen as your teacher reads the story "The Three of Them." Your teacher will stop about halfway through and ask you to make a prediction by answering the first question below.

1. Who do you think "the three of them" are?

_____

After your teacher finishes reading "The Three of Them," answer the second question below.

2. What was the surprise in the story?

_____

Now your teacher will read "The Three of Them" again. Listen carefully and then answer the question below.

3. What clues did the author give you about the identity of "the three of them"?

Acknowledgments

"How Far Away?" from *Tigers at Twilight: Magic Tree House #19* by Mary Pope Osborne. Copyright © 1999 by Mary Pope Osborne. Used by permission of Random House Children's Books, a division of Random House, Inc.

"Lion Ghosts of Africa" by Margaret G. Zackowitz. Copyright © 2002 by National Geographic Society.

from *Sarah, Plain and Tall* by Patricia MacLachlan. Copyright © 1985 by Patricia MacLachlan. Used by permission of HarperCollins Publishers.

"Teacher's Pet" from *Marvin Redpost: Alone in His Teacher's House* by Louis Sachar. Copyright © 1994 by Louis Sachar. Used by permission of Random House Children's Books, a division of Random House, Inc.